POSTCARD PROJECTS

Creative Ideas for Studying Our 50 States

By Linda Wilbur and Barbara Shepard

Illustrated by Gary Hoover

Good Apple, Inc.
299 Jefferson Road
P.O. Box 480
Parsippany, NJ 07054-0480
An imprint of Paramount Supplemental Education

Executive Editor: **Carolea Williams**

Editor: **Ema Arcellana**

Copy Editor: **Susan Eddy**

Design: **Marek/Janci Design**

ISBN 0-86653-836-4

Printed in the United States of America
1. 9 8 7 6 5 4 3 2

CONTENTS

INTRODUCTION

Postcard Projects: Creative Ideas for Studying Our 50 States provides you with hundreds of activities to give your students a comprehensive look at the fifty states. The projects in this resource focus on the development of U.S. history and geography facts as well as the enhancement of research, writing, and higher-level thinking skills.

There are six "postcards" for each state. The first postcard contains general information about the state, such as the capital, state flower, size, and the date the state was admitted to the Union. The other five postcards for each state describe engaging, hands-on projects. Each project card includes a fact about a state and an activity related to that fact. To accommodate all learning styles, the types of projects vary from writing reports and letters to designing postcards and brochures, making models, and conducting interviews.

You might want to reproduce the postcards and affix them to blank 5" x 8" index cards. Laminate the cards for greater durability and store them in a file card box. Or make individualized copies of the project cards that students can keep and refer to as they work. You may want to assign projects to students or invite students to choose their own projects. Students may work alone, in pairs, or in small groups.

Set up a center where students will have easy access to a variety of materials they will need to successfully complete the projects. Materials might include posterboard, white art paper, various sizes of writing paper, glue, scissors, colored pens and pencils, paints, and string. In addition, to a materials center, it would be beneficial to have a computer and printer readily available for student use. Whenever possible, encourage students to use word processing and desktop publishing capabilities to write reports, make posters, and create charts.

We hope your students enjoy these projects as much as our students have and in the process grow in their appreciation for the diversity and wonder of the United States.

RESEARCH SUGGESTIONS

Students will be asked to do research and gather information to complete most projects. Encourage students to use a variety of sources and continue searching when one source does not yield the information they need. It's a good idea to brainstorm all possible sources of information with students before starting a project. Compiling and posting a list of sources will be helpful to your students.

State Resource File

State tourism bureaus and city chambers of commerce will usually send students or teachers packets of information. Addresses for state departments of tourism are usually found in almanacs. The materials are free, but be sure to write well in advance of the time the materials will be needed. You may want to compile a file of these resources yourself or have students do a letter-writing assignment and collect information for a classroom file before beginning the postcard projects.

Vertical Files

The librarian in your school may already have the packets of information mentioned above in a vertical file. Since students often neglect this area of the library when they are searching for information, be sure to remind them to ask the librarian where the vertical files are located.

Books

Most libraries have an abundance of written material about the fifty states. Encourage students to check the school library for all possible sources including encyclopedias, atlases, almanacs, travel guides, books on specific states and regions, and books about state parks and historical areas. It's a good idea to compile a list of these sources or have students compile a list to share with the class.

Multi-Media Encyclopedias

As technology continues to advance, more and more sources are becoming available through the use of the computer. Be sure students check the available encyclopedias, almanacs, atlases, and on-line sources for information on the states.

DISPLAYING AND SHARING PROJECTS

Presenting work for an audience is an important part of student research and displaying work should be encouraged. These types of projects offer excellent opportunities to introduce a variety of display methods to students. Discuss various ways to make work look neat and attractive, such as using varied lettering, colored paper, and mounting and framing techniques. Students may set up displays in several different fashions. Some possibilities include clotheslines, project cubes, tri-fold cardboard backdrops, zig-zag cardboard backdrops, or bulletin boards. Encourage creativity and inventiveness as students develop their own display techniques.

Some ways to share projects include the following.

• Set up a display in the classroom for other classes in the school to view on a certain day.

• Set up displays in the library or on bulletin boards around the building.

• Have a display for parents at open houses or curriculum fairs.

• Use a museum format in hallways to display work so other students or classes may "tour" the United States. Invite students to act as tour guides for the exhibition.

USA MAP

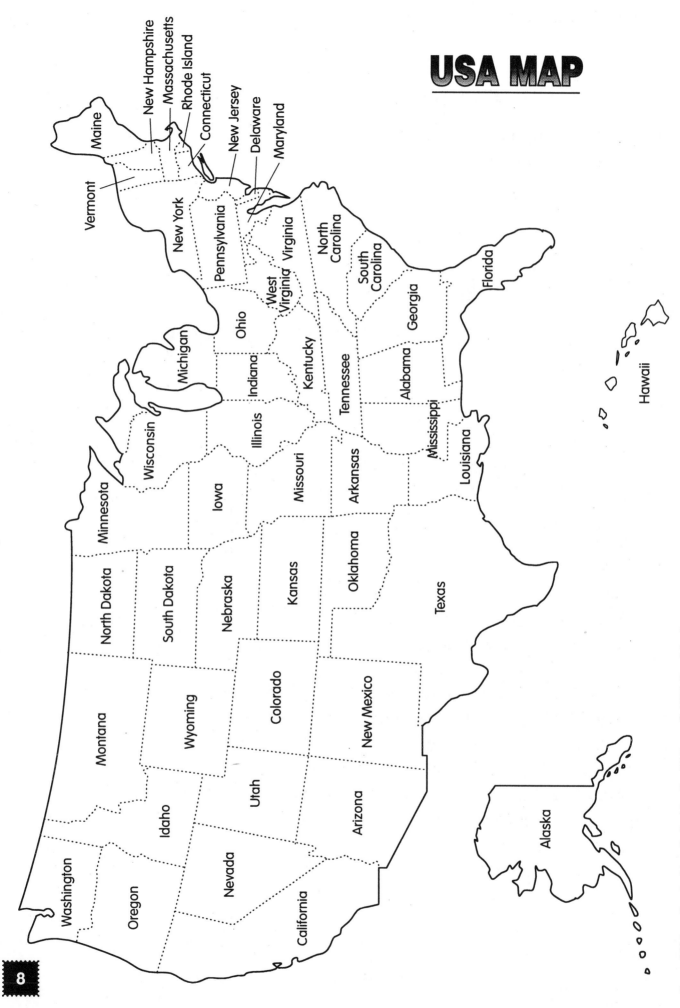

New Hampshire
Massachusetts
Rhode Island
Connecticut
New Jersey
Delaware
Maryland

Maine

Vermont

New York

Pennsylvania

West Virginia

Virginia

North Carolina

South Carolina

Florida

Ohio

Michigan

Indiana

Kentucky

Tennessee

Georgia

Alabama

Mississippi

Louisiana

Wisconsin

Illinois

Missouri

Arkansas

Minnesota

Iowa

Oklahoma

Texas

North Dakota

South Dakota

Nebraska

Kansas

Montana

Wyoming

Colorado

New Mexico

Idaho

Utah

Arizona

Washington

Oregon

Nevada

California

Hawaii

Alaska

8

Postcard Projects: Creative Ideas for Studying Our 50 States © 1995 Good Apple

Capital – **Montgomery**

Size – **50,766 square miles (rank: 28)**

Statehood – **December 14, 1819 (22nd state)**

Song – **"Alabama"**

Bird – **Yellowhammer**

Flower – **Camellia**

Tree – **Southern pine**

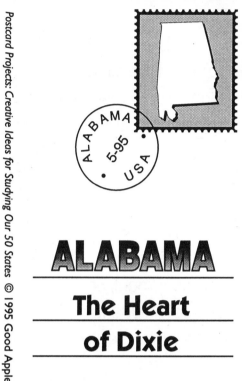

Postcard Projects: Creative Ideas for Studying Our 50 States © 1995 Good Apple

ALABAMA

The Heart of Dixie

The Alabama Space and Rocket Center is located in Huntsville. Make a time line showing the accomplishments of the American Space Program.

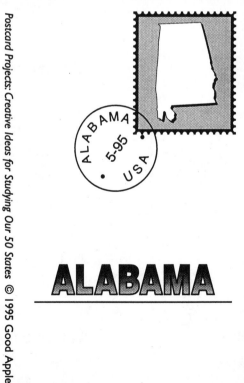

Postcard Projects: Creative Ideas for Studying Our 50 States © 1995 Good Apple

ALABAMA

Wilson Dam is located in the northwest corner of the state and is a National Historic Monument. Research some interesting facts about Wilson Dam. Write a short mystery story centered around this monument. Be sure to include facts and well as creative fiction in your story.

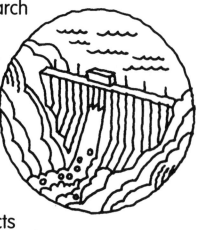

Postcard Projects: Creative Ideas for Studying Our 50 States © 1995 Good Apple

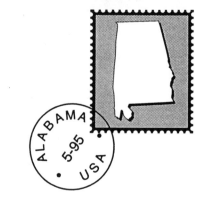

ALABAMA _____

Cliff-dwelling Indians lived in Jackson County in what is now Russell Cave National Monument over 8000 years ago. Do some research to find out what excavations at this site have revealed about the lives of these Indians. Share your findings in an illustrated report.

Postcard Projects: Creative Ideas for Studying Our 50 States © 1995 Good Apple

ALABAMA _____

Arlington is Birmingham's only antebellum home. Find out what an antebellum home is. Design a postcard of an antebellum home. Draw a picture on one side of the card and write a description of the home on the reverse side.

Postcard Projects: Creative Ideas for Studying Our 50 States © 1995 Good Apple

ALABAMA

Jefferson Davis' home, the "First White House" of the Confederacy, can be found in the capital city of Montgomery. Write a report about the President of the Confederacy, Jefferson Davis.

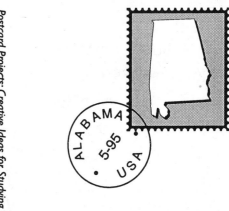

Postcard Projects: Creative Ideas for Studying Our 50 States © 1995 Good Apple

ALABAMA

Capital – **Juneau**

Size – **570,833 square miles (rank: 1)**

Statehood – **January 3, 1959 (49th state)**

Song – **"Alaska's Flag"**

Bird – **Willow ptarmigan**

Flower – **Forget-me-not**

Tree – **Sitka spruce**

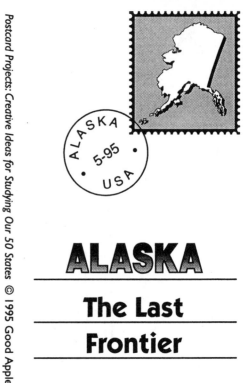

Postcard Projects: Creative Ideas for Studying Our 50 States © 1995 Good Apple

ALASKA

The Last Frontier

Alaska had three gold rushes — 1896 (Klondike), 1899 (Nome), and 1902 (Fairbanks). Read about one of these gold rushes and imagine what it would have been like to live during that time period. Write several journal entries describing what your life might have been like.

Postcard Projects: Creative Ideas for Studying Our 50 States © 1995 Good Apple

ALASKA

Eskimos are native to Alaska. They have devised a great variety of indoor games to help pass the many long hours of winter darkness. Find out how some of these games are played. Then make the equipment you need, teach the game to a friend, and give a demonstration to the class.

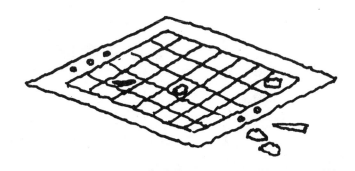

Postcard Projects: Creative Ideas for Studying Our 50 States © 1995 Good Apple

ALASKA _____

Scientists believe Alaska was once connected to Russia by a land bridge. Draw a map showing where scientists believe the land bridge was. Include information that tells what may have happened to this land bridge.

Postcard Projects: Creative Ideas for Studying Our 50 States © 1995 Good Apple

ALASKA _____

The Trans-Alaska Pipeline carries oil 800 miles from Prudhoe Bay to Valdez. Construction began in 1974 and lasted three years. Draw a map of Alaska and use flexible straws to mark the route of the pipeline. Then write a short paragraph explaining the significance of the pipeline to Alaska.

Postcard Projects: Creative Ideas for Studying Our 50 States © 1995 Good Apple

ALASKA

ALASKA
5-95
USA

Each year, Nome sponsors the Iditarod Dog Sled Classic. Design a registration form for the event. Don't forget to include all pertinent information, such as what, where, when, why, and who.

Postcard Projects: Creative Ideas for Studying Our 50 States © 1995 Good Apple

ALASKA

ALASKA
5-95
USA

Capital – **Phoenix**

Size – **113,510 square miles
(rank: 6)**

Statehood – **February 14, 1912
(48th state)**

Song – **"Arizona"**

Bird – **Cactus wren**

Flower – **Saguaro cactus flower**

Tree – **Palo verde**

Postcard Projects: Creative Ideas for Studying Our 50 States © 1995 Good Apple

ARIZONA

The Grand
Canyon State

The Navaho National Monument is the site of two of the largest cliff dwellings ever discovered. Find out what these cliff dwellings looked like. Use the information you gather to make an authentic-looking diorama of a cliff dwelling.

Postcard Projects: Creative Ideas for Studying Our 50 States © 1995 Good Apple

ARIZONA

Because of its large desert area, Arizona is home to many varieties of cacti. Make an illustrated chart showing at least ten types of cacti and their flowers.

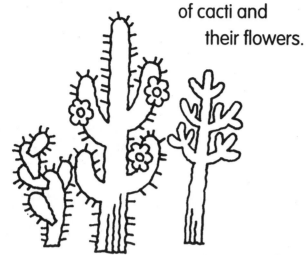

Postcard Projects: Creative Ideas for Studying Our 50 States © 1995 Good Apple

ARIZONA

Tucson is known as the "Astronomy Capital of the World." Find out why and how Tucson got this name. Write a story telling about a UFO landing in Tucson. Include some facts you discovered in your research as well as creative fiction.

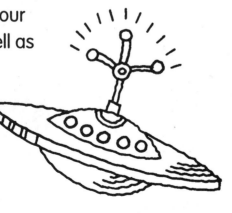

Postcard Projects: Creative Ideas for Studying Our 50 States © 1995 Good Apple

ARIZONA

Hoover Dam on the Colorado River supplies water and electric power for a good part of the Pacific Southwest. Build a scale model or draw a cutaway view of the dam. Prepare a short oral report explaining how a dam generates electricity from water power.

Postcard Projects: Creative Ideas for Studying Our 50 States © 1995 Good Apple

ARIZONA

The Grand Canyon is an immense gorge cut by the Colorado River into the high plateau in the northern part of Arizona. Listen to the "Grand Canyon Suite" by Grofé. Choose one of the pieces and illustrate it.

Postcard Projects: Creative Ideas for Studying Our 50 States © 1995 Good Apple

ARIZONA

Capital – **Little Rock**

Size – **52,082 square miles
(rank: 27)**

Statehood – **June 15, 1836
(25th state)**

Song – **"Arkansas"**

Bird – **Mockingbird**

Flower – **Apple blossom**

Tree – **Pine**

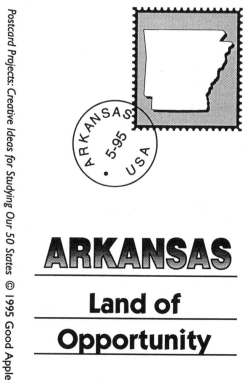

Postcard Projects: Creative Ideas for Studying Our 50 States © 1995 Good Apple

ARKANSAS

Land of
Opportunity

Arkansas has two nicknames — "Land of Opportunity" and "The Natural State." Working with a partner (taking opposite sides) develop reasons for both nicknames and present your arguments to the class. Invite the class to vote on the more appropriate nickname.

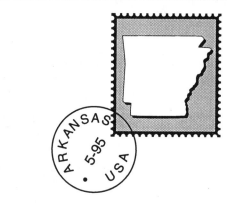

Postcard Projects: Creative Ideas for Studying Our 50 States © 1995 Good Apple

ARKANSAS

Hot Springs National Park is famous for its mineral springs. President Franklin Roosevelt frequently visited the springs to help improve his health. Interview a doctor to find out about the effects of mineral springs on people's health. Present your findings to the class in an oral report.

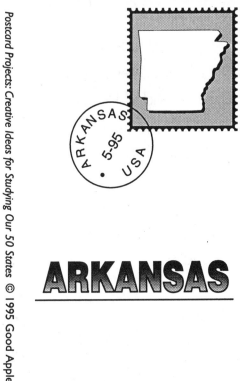

Postcard Projects: Creative Ideas for Studying Our 50 States © 1995 Good Apple

ARKANSAS

Fort Smith, one of the earliest forts of the American West, was founded in 1817. The reconstructed Fort Smith National Historic Site preserves the tales about wagon trains heading west. Create a map showing the wagon train trails. Make a list of supplies often carried by travelers.

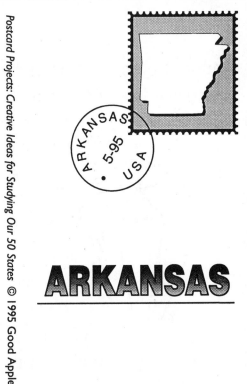

Postcard Projects: Creative Ideas for Studying Our 50 States © 1995 Good Apple

ARKANSAS

Near Mountain View are the Blanchard Springs Caverns which are known as the "Cave Find of the Century." Pretend you are a spelunker. Create a travel brochure for other spelunkers telling what they will see and what kind of equipment they will need to explore the caverns. Explain why each piece of equipment is important.

Postcard Projects: Creative Ideas for Studying Our 50 States © 1995 Good Apple

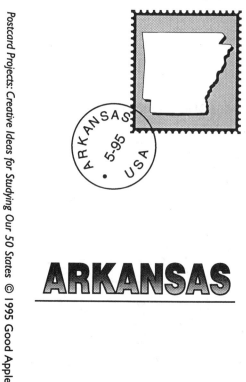

ARKANSAS

In Crater of Diamonds State Park near Murfreesboro is a diamond mine that was discovered in 1906. The mine was mined commercially for about a decade. Now, visitors can search for diamonds when they visit the park. Make a chart telling how diamonds are formed. Include information about the types and qualities of diamonds.

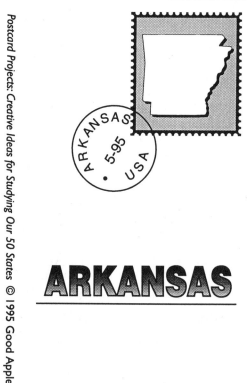

Postcard Projects: Creative Ideas for Studying Our 50 States © 1995 Good Apple

ARKANSAS

Capital – **Sacramento**

Size – **156,297 square miles (rank: 3)**

Statehood – **September 9, 1850 (31st state)**

Song – **"I Love You, California"**

Bird – **California valley quail**

Flower – **Golden poppy**

Tree – **California redwood**

Postcard Projects: Creative Ideas for Studying Our 50 States © 1995 Good Apple

CALIFORNIA 5-95 USA

CALIFORNIA

The Golden State

In 1906 and again in 1989, San Francisco was badly damaged by earthquakes. Find out what causes earthquakes and why San Francisco has experienced such severe ones. Make models of several types of faults and compare them.

Postcard Projects: Creative Ideas for Studying Our 50 States © 1995 Good Apple

CALIFORNIA 5-95 USA

CALIFORNIA

Death Valley is located in Southern California near the Nevada border. In a travel brochure, tell why this region is called Death Valley. Don't forget to include detailed descriptions and illustrations of the area.

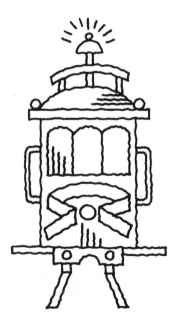

Postcard Projects: Creative Ideas for Studying Our 50 States © 1995 Good Apple

CALIFORNIA

The cable car was invented in 1873 in San Francisco and is still a picturesque part of the city. Find out the name of the inventor. What feature of the San Francisco landscape was the cable car especially well suited for? Draw a cable car and answer these questions in a paragraph beneath your illustration.

Postcard Projects: Creative Ideas for Studying Our 50 States © 1995 Good Apple

CALIFORNIA

In 1932 and 1984, the Olympic Games were held in Los Angeles. Make a Venn diagram or graph comparing the number of various medals won by the United States in these two sets of games.

Postcard Projects: Creative Ideas for Studying Our 50 States © 1995 Good Apple

CALIFORNIA

The 49'ers headed to California in search of gold. The first authenticated discovery of gold, however, was made near Los Angeles in 1842. Read about the 49'ers and life in the gold fields. Imagine you were a 49'er searching for gold and write a diary describing your life.

Postcard Projects: Creative Ideas for Studying Our 50 States © 1995 Good Apple

CALIFORNIA

Capital – **Denver**

Size – **103,598 square miles
(rank: 8)**

Statehood – **August 1, 1876
(38th state)**

Song – **"Where the
Columbines Grow"**

Bird – **Lark bunting**

Flower – **Rocky Mountain columbine**

Tree – **Colorado blue spruce**

Postcard Projects: Creative Ideas for Studying Our 50 States © 1995 Good Apple

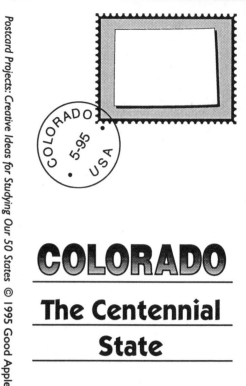

COLORADO
<COLORADO 5-95 USA>

COLORADO
The Centennial State

Pike's Peak is a famous landmark in Colorado named after Zebulon Pike. Find out about Zebulon Pike and make a time line of his life.

Postcard Projects: Creative Ideas for Studying Our 50 States © 1995 Good Apple

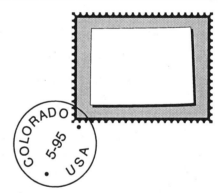

COLORADO
<COLORADO 5-95 USA>

COLORADO

In Denver you can visit the United States Mint where coins are made. Find out how the designs for the penny, dime, nickel, quarter, and half dollar progress from illustration to actual coins. Design a new coin for a denom- ination you feel would be useful. Include in your design something significant to Colorado.

Postcard Projects: Creative Ideas for Studying Our 50 States © 1995 Good Apple

COLORADO

M esa Verde National Park is the site of the cliff dwellings of the early Pueblo Indians, the Anasazi. Find out about these Native Americans and write an illustrated report about your findings.

ANASAZI

Postcard Projects: Creative Ideas for Studying Our 50 States © 1995 Good Apple

COLORADO

At Dinosaur National Park you can watch paleontologists at work uncovering the fossilized remains of creatures that lived millions of years ago. Find out what kinds of dinosaurs lived in Colorado. Make a clay model of each dinosaur. Write its name, size, and the era during which it inhabited the region on a file card.

Postcard Projects: Creative Ideas for Studying Our 50 States © 1995 Good Apple

COLORADO · 5-95 · USA

COLORADO

Black Hawk, one of the earliest mining towns, is located west of Denver. Today, Black Hawk is a ghost town. Many ghost towns can still be found in Colorado. Write a story about a "ghost" who might live in one of these abandoned towns. Illustrate your story.

Postcard Projects: Creative Ideas for Studying Our 50 States © 1995 Good Apple

COLORADO · 5-95 · USA

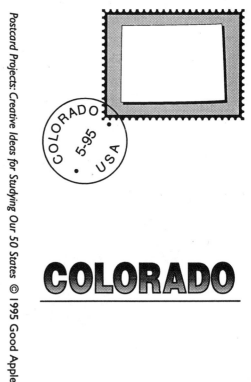

COLORADO

Capital – **Hartford**

Size – **4,872 square miles (rank: 48)**

Statehood – **January 9, 1788 (5th state)**

Song – **"Yankee Doodle"**

Bird – **American robin**

Flower – **Mountain laurel**

Tree – **White oak**

Postcard Projects: Creative Ideas for Studying Our 50 States © 1995 Good Apple

CONNECTICUT
The Constitution State

Near Hartford is the saltbox home of Noah Webster who compiled the first dictionary. Find out about this unique New England style of architecture. Build a model of a saltbox home.

FIRST DICTIONARY

Postcard Projects: Creative Ideas for Studying Our 50 States © 1995 Good Apple

CONNECTICUT

The *Nautilus*, the world's first nuclear-powered submarine, was built in Groton and launched in 1954. Visitors can go aboard at the U.S.S. Nautilus Memorial and explore the submarine. Do some research on submarines. Build a working model which you can use to demonstrate to the class how submarines sink and rise.

Postcard Projects: Creative Ideas for Studying Our 50 States © 1995 Good Apple

CONNECTICUT

Mystic Seaport and Aquarium, a popular tourist attraction in Mystic, contains a reconstruction of a waterfront village from the mid-1800's — the days of the famous old sailing ships. Do some research on clipper ships and the lives of their sailors. Build a detailed model or draw a detailed illustration of a clipper ship.

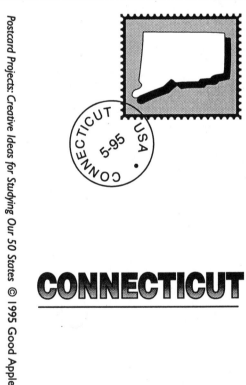

Postcard Projects: Creative Ideas for Studying Our 50 States © 1995 Good Apple

CONNECTICUT

On the south side of Hartford is the Colt Patent Firearms Company. Research the history of the Colt revolvers and find out why they are known as "the guns that won the West." Write a report about what you learned.

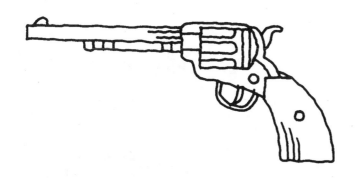

Postcard Projects: Creative Ideas for Studying Our 50 States © 1995 Good Apple

CONNECTICUT

Fort Griswold State Park is the site of the massacre of Americans in 1781 by British soldiers under the command of traitor Benedict

Arnold. Make a "Wanted" poster of Benedict Arnold. Include relevant information, such as a physical description of Arnold and why he was wanted.

Postcard Projects: Creative Ideas for Studying Our 50 States © 1995 Good Apple

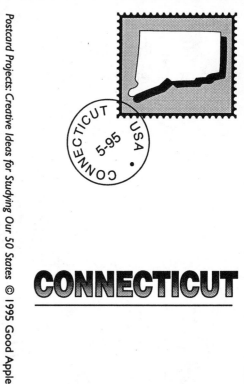

CONNECTICUT

Capital – **Dover**

Size – **1,933 square miles (rank: 49)**

Statehood – **December 7, 1787 (1st state)**

Song – **"Our Delaware"**

Bird – **Blue hen chicken**

Flower – **Peach blossom**

Tree – **American holly**

Postcard Projects: Creative Ideas for Studying Our 50 States © 1995 Good Apple

DELAWARE

The First

State

É leuthère Irénée duPont established a gun powder mill on Brandywine Creek. This mill became the foundation of Delaware's chemical industry. The duPonts are still an important family in Delaware. Make a family tree of E.I. duPont's important descendants and give a short description of their contributions.

Postcard Projects: Creative Ideas for Studying Our 50 States © 1995 Good Apple

DELAWARE

In 1683, Swedish and Finnish immigrants brought the log cabin to Delaware Valley and to the New World. This type of home became common throughout the settling of the United States. Build a model of a log cabin and write a list of the advantages and disadvantages of this type of building.

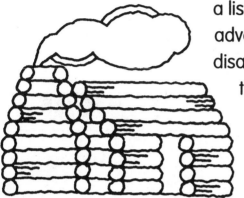

Postcard Projects: Creative Ideas for Studying Our 50 States © 1995 Good Apple

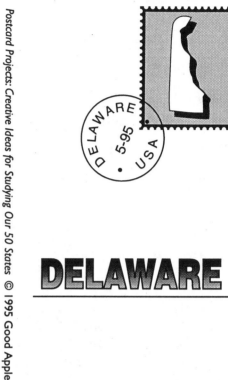

DELAWARE
5-95
USA

DELAWARE

The northern border of Delaware is the arc of a perfect circle whose center is the dome of the Court House in New Castle. Obtain a map of Delaware and locate the Court House using a compass. Write a paragraph explaining the reason for this boundary — the only one like it in the country.

Postcard Projects: Creative Ideas for Studying Our 50 States © 1995 Good Apple

DELAWARE
5-95
USA

DELAWARE

The town of Wilmington was settled by the New Sweden Company in 1638. Find out why this Swedish company came to America and what they hoped for in the New World. Write a newspaper article pretending you are one of these early Swedish settlers. Be sure to include the five W's — who, what, why, where, and when.

Postcard Projects: Creative Ideas for Studying Our 50 States © 1995 Good Apple

DELAWARE · 5-95 · USA

DELAWARE

On July 5, 1776, Caesar Rodney rode from Dover, Delaware to Philadelphia, Pennsylvania to break the tie vote for independence. Write a short report about this man and his famous trip. In addition, draw a map of his route.

Postcard Projects: Creative Ideas for Studying Our 50 States © 1995 Good Apple

DELAWARE · 5-95 · USA

DELAWARE

Capital – **Tallahassee**

Size – **54,157 square miles (rank: 26)**

Statehood – **March 3, 1845 (27th state)**

Song – **"Old Folks at Home"**

Bird – **Mockingbird**

Flower – **Orange blossom**

Tree – **Palmetto palm**

FLORIDA

The Sunshine State

Jai-alai is a game widely played in Spain. In the United States, it is most popular in Florida. Find out how to play jai-alai and teach some of your friends.

FLORIDA

St. Augustine, founded in 1565, is the oldest city in the United States. Read about the Castillo de San Marcos. Build a model of the fort including the moat.

Postcard Projects: Creative Ideas for Studying Our 50 States © 1995 Good Apple

FLORIDA

The Florida Keys form the southern-most part of the United States. Make a travel brochure of the Keys. Include in your brochure a brief history of the area and any sites you would recommend for tourists to visit.

Postcard Projects: Creative Ideas for Studying Our 50 States © 1995 Good Apple

FLORIDA

When Ponce de Leon discovered Florida in 1513, he was looking for the Fountain of Youth. Read about Ponce de Leon's search. Write a story pretending that he actually found the Fountain of Youth and how his discovery changed history.

Postcard Projects: Creative Ideas for Studying Our 50 States © 1995 Good Apple

FLORIDA

FLORIDA 5-95 USA

Epcot Center, Walt Disney World, and Sea World are all located near Orlando. Choose another city in Florida that you think would make a great place for a tourist attraction. Invent another theme park. Describe where it would be located in Florida. Draw maps showing tourists how to get to your new theme park from five other major cities in Florida.

Postcard Projects: Creative Ideas for Studying Our 50 States © 1995 Good Apple

FLORIDA

FLORIDA 5-95 USA

Capital – **Atlanta**

Size – **58,060 square miles (rank: 21)**

Statehood – **January 2, 1788 (4th state)**

Song – **"Georgia on My Mind"**

Bird – **Brown thrasher**

Flower – **Cherokee rose**

Tree – **Live oak**

Postcard Projects: Creative Ideas for Studying Our 50 States © 1995 Good Apple

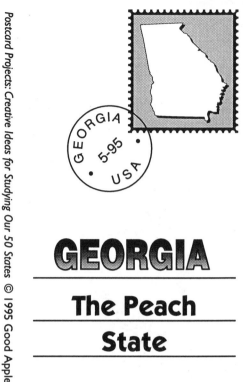

GEORGIA

The Peach
State

The Okefenokee Swamp is a state park. Find out about swamp environments and write an editorial telling why they should be preserved and protected.

Postcard Projects: Creative Ideas for Studying Our 50 States © 1995 Good Apple

GEORGIA

Juliette Gordon Low, founder of the Girl Scouts, was born in Savannah. Read a biography about Mrs. Low and make a storyboard illustrating her life.

Postcard Projects: Creative Ideas for Studying Our 50 States © 1995 Good Apple

GEORGIA

5-95

USA

GEORGIA

Stone Mountain is the world's largest mass of exposed granite. Carved on the side of Stone Mountain are the personages Robert E. Lee, Stonewall Jackson, and Jefferson Davis. Choose another person from Southern history who you would add to Stone Mountain if you could. Write a paragraph defending your choice.

STONE MOUNTAIN

Postcard Projects: Creative Ideas for Studying Our 50 States © 1995 Good Apple

GEORGIA

5-95

USA

GEORGIA

During the Civil War, General Sherman "marched" through Georgia. Make a map of Georgia showing this march. Include on the map brief descriptions of what Sherman encountered along his way.

Postcard Projects: Creative Ideas for Studying Our 50 States © 1995 Good Apple

GEORGIA
5-95
USA

GEORGIA

Georgia was founded by James Oglethorpe. Find out about the founding of Georgia. Pretend you are James Oglethorpe and keep a journal about this early period.

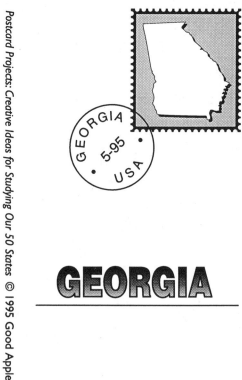

JOURNAL

JAMES OGLETHORPE

Postcard Projects: Creative Ideas for Studying Our 50 States © 1995 Good Apple

GEORGIA
5-95
USA

GEORGIA

Capital – **Honolulu**

Size – **6,427 square miles**
(rank: 47)

Statehood – **August 21, 1959**
(50th state)

Song – **"Hawaii Ponoi"**

Bird – **Hawaiian goose**

Flower – **Hibiscus**

Tree – **Candlenut**

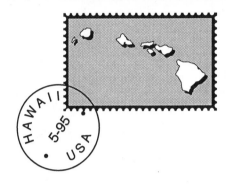

Postcard Projects: Creative Ideas for Studying Our 50 States © 1995 Good Apple

HAWAII 5-95 USA

HAWAII

The Aloha
State

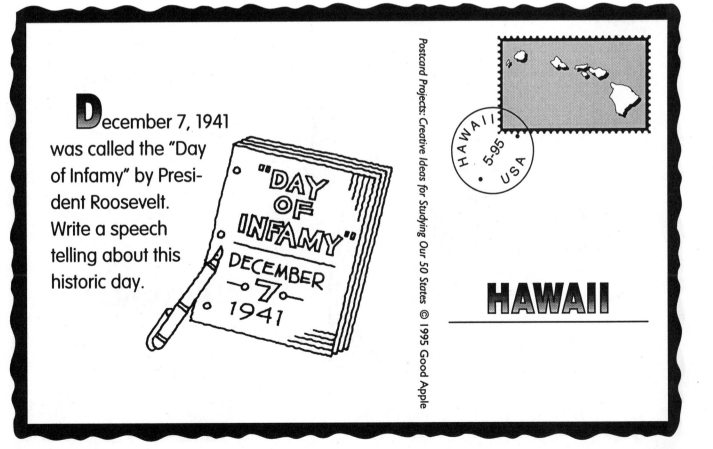

December 7, 1941 was called the "Day of Infamy" by President Roosevelt. Write a speech telling about this historic day.

"DAY OF INFAMY"
DECEMBER 7 1941

Postcard Projects: Creative Ideas for Studying Our 50 States © 1995 Good Apple

HAWAII 5-95 USA

HAWAII

Hawaii has many customs that are unique to the state. Write and illustrate a book about some of these Hawaiian customs.

Postcard Projects: Creative Ideas for Studying Our 50 States © 1995 Good Apple

HAWAII

Hawaii was once ruled by kings and queens. Read about the royalty of Hawaii. Make illustrations of the native royal clothing.

Postcard Projects: Creative Ideas for Studying Our 50 States © 1995 Good Apple

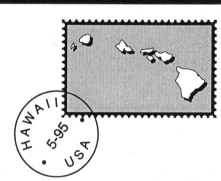

HAWAII

The Hawaiian alphabet has only 12 letters. Find out what they are. Learn 12 words in Hawaiian and write them in an illustrated dictionary, along with the appropriate Hawaiian spelling rules. Include at least three full sentences as well.

Postcard Projects: Creative Ideas for Studying Our 50 States © 1995 Good Apple

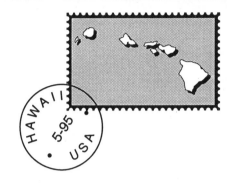

HAWAII

Legend says the Hawaiian islands were formed when Maui, one of the gods, put his fishhook into the sea and pulled up the islands. The islands of Hawaii were actually formed by volcanoes. Read about the forming of these islands. Make a drawing that illustrates how an island is formed from a volcano.

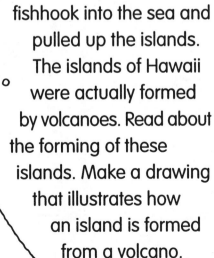

Postcard Projects: Creative Ideas for Studying Our 50 States © 1995 Good Apple

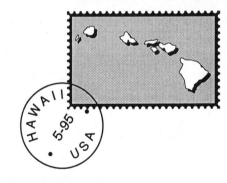

HAWAII

Capital – **Boise**

Size – **82,413 square miles**
(rank: 11)

Statehood – **July 3, 1890**
(43rd state)

Song – **"Here We Have Idaho"**

Bird – **Mountain bluebird**

Flower – **Idaho syringa**

Tree – **White pine**

Postcard Projects: Creative Ideas for Studying Our 50 States © 1995 Good Apple

IDAHO

The Gem

State

There are many national forests in the state of Idaho. Write an editorial that could be presented on radio or television stating why these forests should be preserved.

Postcard Projects: Creative Ideas for Studying Our 50 States © 1995 Good Apple

IDAHO

The Nez Perce was one of the largest Native American tribes to live in Idaho. Read about this tribe and build a model of the type of housing in which they lived.

Postcard Projects: Creative Ideas for Studying Our 50 States © 1995 Good Apple

IDAHO
_____

Although pioneer settlers scorned its forbidding land, Idaho has become one of the country's most prosperous agricultural areas and produces more potatoes than any other state. Create a topographical map of Idaho. In an oral presentation, show where potatoes are grown and demonstrate how the Snake River is crucial to Idaho's agriculture.

Postcard Projects: Creative Ideas for Studying Our 50 States © 1995 Good Apple

IDAHO
_____

The Lewiston Roundup is a rodeo held the first weekend after Labor Day in Lewiston. Find out how rodeos began and how they are different or similar to rodeos today. Make a chart comparing rodeo events in the past and present.

Postcard Projects: Creative Ideas for Studying Our 50 States © 1995 Good Apple

IDAHO

Sun Valley is Idaho's most famous resort. Write to Idaho Tourism, Room 108, Statehouse, Boise, Idaho 83707. Ask for information about Sun Valley. When your information arrives, plan a week-long vacation there and make an itinerary of your activities.

Postcard Projects: Creative Ideas for Studying Our 50 States © 1995 Good Apple

IDAHO

Capital – **Springfield**

Size – **55,646 square miles (rank: 24)**

Statehood – **December 3, 1818 (21st state)**

Song – **"Illinois"**

Bird – **Cardinal**

Flower – **Illinois native violet**

Tree – **White oak**

Postcard Projects: Creative Ideas for Studying Our 50 States © 1995 Good Apple

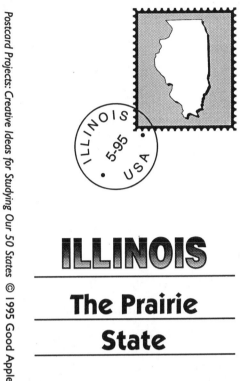

ILLINOIS

The Prairie State

John Deere and Cyrus McCormick are two innovators in the history of Illinois manufacturing and production. Research their inventions. Describe the effects of their inventions on agriculture. Draw a picture of the way their inventions looked in the 1800's and the way they look today.

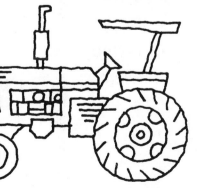

Postcard Projects: Creative Ideas for Studying Our 50 States © 1995 Good Apple

ILLINOIS

Abraham Lincoln, our 16th president, lived in Illinois. On a map of Illinois, mark the places where Lincoln lived. Make a time line showing when he lived in each place and the events that occurred in his life while he lived there.

Postcard Projects: Creative Ideas for Studying Our 50 States © 1995 Good Apple

ILLINOIS _____

The disastrous Chicago fire of 1871 was said to have been started by Mrs. O'Leary's cow. Read about this historic fire. Why was this fire so devastating? Make a fire safety brochure that tells important information that could prevent such disasters in the future.

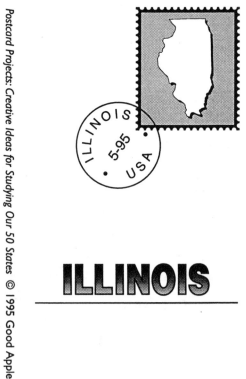

WHOOPS

Postcard Projects: Creative Ideas for Studying Our 50 States © 1995 Good Apple

ILLINOIS _____

Nauvoo was named and established as the Mormon religious capital by John Smith in 1839. Find out about the various moves the Mormons made until they settled in Utah and make a map of their travels.

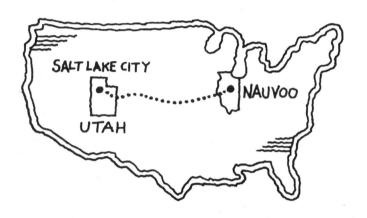

Postcard Projects: Creative Ideas for Studying Our 50 States © 1995 Good Apple

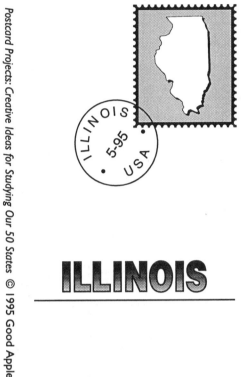

ILLINOIS

Frank Lloyd Wright, one of the most famous architects of the twentieth century, was from Chicago. Look at some pictures of his work. Draw or make a model of a house or building in a similar style.

Postcard Projects: Creative Ideas for Studying Our 50 States © 1995 Good Apple

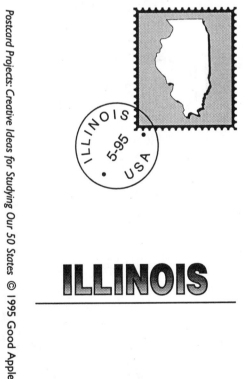

ILLINOIS

Capital – **Indianapolis**

Size – **35,936 square miles**
(rank: 38)

Statehood – **December 11, 1816**
(19th state)

Song – **"On the Banks of the**
Wabash, Far Away"

Bird – **Cardinal**

Flower – **Peony**

Tree – **Tulip tree**

Postcard Projects: Creative Ideas for Studying Our 50 States © 1995 Good Apple

INDIANA

The Hoosier
State

In 1787, Indiana became part of the Northwest Territory. Read about Indiana and the Northwest Territory. Make a mobile demonstrating what you learned. Be sure to include what the Northwest Territory was, how Indiana became a part of it, and who the important people were in the transaction.

Postcard Projects: Creative Ideas for Studying Our 50 States © 1995 Good Apple

INDIANA

Each Memorial Day, Indianapolis hosts the Indianapolis 500 auto race. Beginning with 1970, make a line graph showing the winning speed each year.

Postcard Projects: Creative Ideas for Studying Our 50 States © 1995 Good Apple

INDIANA

There are many famous sites in Indiana. Some of the places to visit include Studebaker National Museum, George Rogers Clark National Historic Park, French Lick, Hoosier Dome, and Wyandotte Cave. Choose four sites and make a poster divided into four sections that highlights each.

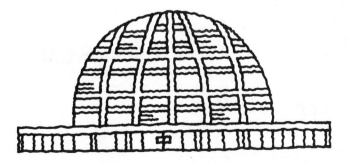

Postcard Projects: Creative Ideas for Studying Our 50 States © 1995 Good Apple

INDIANA

In 1825, Robert Owen bought land and began New Harmony, an experimental community for a Utopian society. Make a Venn diagram comparing your community with a New Harmony-like Utopian society.

Postcard Projects: Creative Ideas for Studying Our 50 States © 1995 Good Apple

INDIANA

The French fur traders were among the first to explore the land that is Indiana today. Make a poster showing what items they used to trade for furs. Also, list the types of furs that were traded.

Postcard Projects: Creative Ideas for Studying Our 50 States © 1995 Good Apple

INDIANA

Capital – **Des Moines**

Size – **55,965 square miles
(rank: 23)**

Statehood – **December 28, 1846
(29th state)**

Song – **"The Song of Iowa"**

Bird – **Eastern goldfinch**

Flower – **Wild rose**

Tree – **Oak**

Postcard Projects: Creative Ideas for Studying Our 50 States © 1995 Good Apple

IOWA
The Hawkeye State

The Mississippi Flyway passes through Iowa. Find out exactly where in Iowa it is and make a map showing your findings.

Postcard Projects: Creative Ideas for Studying Our 50 States © 1995 Good Apple

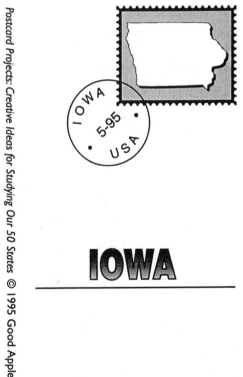

IOWA

The majority of the Iowa population is of German descent. Many of these people live in the Amana Colonies. How did the colonies begin? Write an article for a tourism magazine encouraging people to visit the Amanas.

Postcard Projects: Creative Ideas for Studying Our 50 States © 1995 Good Apple

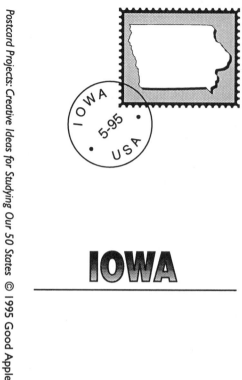

IOWA

_____

The famous lawman Wyatt Earp grew up in Pella, Iowa. Find out about his early years in Pella and make a time line of important events in his life.

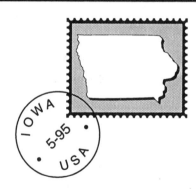

Postcard Projects: Creative Ideas for Studying Our 50 States © 1995 Good Apple

IOWA

_____

"**B**uffalo Bill" Cody was born in Scott County where you can visit a museum that contains memorabilia of his Wild West shows. Design an ad that will attract people to "Wild Bill's" Wild West show.

Postcard Projects: Creative Ideas for Studying Our 50 States © 1995 Good Apple

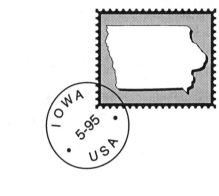

IOWA 5-95 USA

IOWA
_____

Washington County is Amish country. The largest Amish settlement west of Mississippi is near Stone City. Find out about the Amish people. Then design a quilt depicting the Amish people and their way of life.

Postcard Projects: Creative Ideas for Studying Our 50 States © 1995 Good Apple

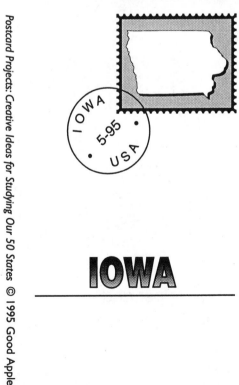

IOWA 5-95 USA

IOWA
_____

Capital – **Topeka**

Size – **81,783 square miles
(rank: 13)**

Statehood – **January 29, 1861
(34th state)**

Song – **"Home on the Range"**

Bird – **Western meadowlark**

Flower – **Sunflower**

Tree – **Cottonwood**

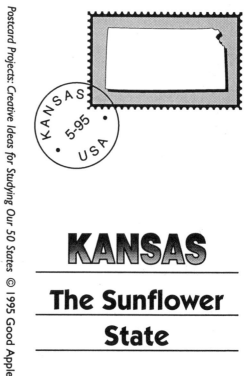

Postcard Projects: Creative Ideas for Studying Our 50 States © 1995 Good Apple

KANSAS

The Sunflower State

Jotham Meeker published a newspaper called the *Shawnee Sun* beginning in 1835. Research the significance of the newspaper and write an article which might have appeared on the front page.

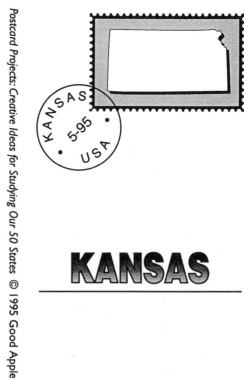

Postcard Projects: Creative Ideas for Studying Our 50 States © 1995 Good Apple

KANSAS

Dodge City became an infamous cow town. Modern Dodge City is a new type of cow town. Research both and decide which one you'd prefer to live in. Defend your choice in an oral presentation.

Postcard Projects: Creative Ideas for Studying Our 50 States © 1995 Good Apple

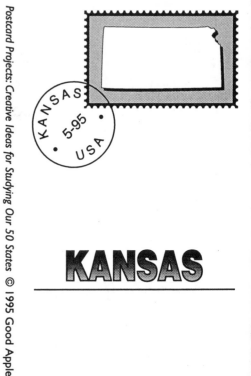

KANSAS
_____

Fort Leavenworth was the starting point for wagon trains heading out on the Oregon and Santa Fe Trails. Make a map showing these trails and a chart that compares and contrasts them.

OREGON AND SANTA FE TRAILS

Postcard Projects: Creative Ideas for Studying Our 50 States © 1995 Good Apple

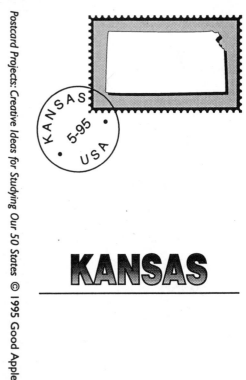

KANSAS
_____

Kansas, the Breadbasket of America, is the largest wheat-producing state in the country. Find out how wheat bread is made

and bake a loaf to share with your class. Also find out the significance of the wheat known as Turkey Red.

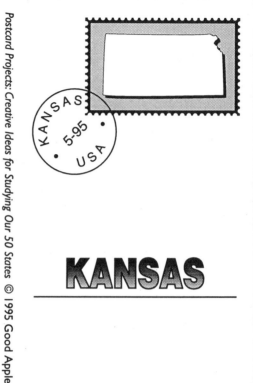

Postcard Projects: Creative Ideas for Studying Our 50 States © 1995 Good Apple

KANSAS
_____

In *The Wizard of Oz*, Dorothy gets caught in a Kansas cyclone. Find out how cyclones form and make an illustrated chart showing what you discovered.

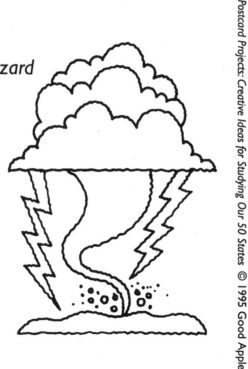

Postcard Projects: Creative Ideas for Studying Our 50 States © 1995 Good Apple

KANSAS
_____

Capital – **Frankfort**

Size – **39,674 square miles**
(rank: 37)

Statehood – **June 1, 1792**
(15th state)

Song – **"My Old Kentucky Home"**

Bird – **Cardinal**

Flower – **Goldenrod**

Tree – **Kentucky coffee tree**

Postcard Projects: Creative Ideas for Studying Our 50 States © 1995 Good Apple

KENTUCKY

The Bluegrass State

One of the most famous horse races in the world, the Kentucky Derby, is run the first Saturday in May at Louisville's Churchill Downs. Research the many traditions associated with the Kentucky Derby and tell about them on an illustrated poster.

Postcard Projects: Creative Ideas for Studying Our 50 States © 1995 Good Apple

KENTUCKY

While in Kentucky, you can visit a mansion called Federal Hill.

The song "My Old Kentucky Home" by Stephen Foster was inspired by the mansion. Listen to the song and draw a picture of how you think Federal Hill might have looked.

Postcard Projects: Creative Ideas for Studying Our 50 States © 1995 Good Apple

KENTUCKY
5-95
USA

KENTUCKY

Lexington prides itself in being the "Horse Center of America." Why does Lexington claim this title? Make a list of facts that support this claim.

KENTUCKY
5-95
USA

Postcard Projects: Creative Ideas for Studying Our 50 States © 1995 Good Apple

KENTUCKY

Mammoth Cave is an internationally-known cave located in Edmonson County. How are caves made? Make a model of a cave and explain what you learned in an oral presentation.

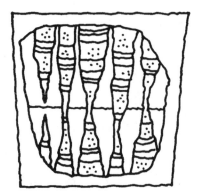

Postcard Projects: Creative Ideas for Studying Our 50 States © 1995 Good Apple

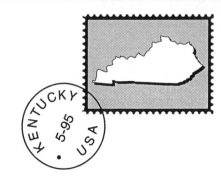

KENTUCKY 5-95 USA

KENTUCKY

Kentucky got its name from a Cherokee word whose possible meaning is *Land of Tomorrow* or *Meadowland*. Which of the meanings do you think is best? Write a paragraph stating your choice and give five supporting reasons.

Postcard Projects: Creative Ideas for Studying Our 50 States © 1995 Good Apple

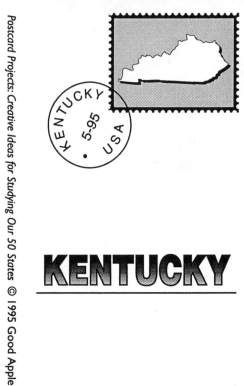

KENTUCKY 5-95 USA

KENTUCKY

Capital – **Baton Rouge**

Size – **44,520 square miles (rank: 33)**

Statehood – **April 30, 1812 (18th state)**

Song – **"Give Me Louisiana"**

Bird – **Brown pelican**

Flower – **Magnolia**

Tree – **Bald cypress**

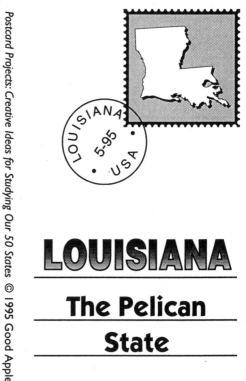

Postcard Projects: Creative Ideas for Studying Our 50 States © 1995 Good Apple

LOUISIANA
The Pelican State

Louisiana has many bayous. Find out about this type of environment and the kinds of plants and animals that are found there. Make a collage of the plants and animals that can be found in a bayou.

Postcard Projects: Creative Ideas for Studying Our 50 States © 1995 Good Apple

LOUISIANA

Spanish moss can be found on many trees in southern Louisiana. Illustrate a tree with Spanish moss on it. Write a description of Spanish moss.

Postcard Projects: Creative Ideas for Studying Our 50 States © 1995 Good Apple

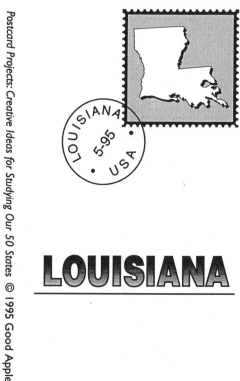

LOUISIANA

Creoles, descendents of the French and Spanish, are known for their distinctive style of cooking. Find a Creole recipe and prepare the dish to share with your class.

Postcard Projects: Creative Ideas for Studying Our 50 States © 1995 Good Apple

LOUISIANA

The city of New Orleans attracts millions of tourists each year. Read about this unique city and its annual Mardi Gras. Create a Mardi Gras mask to wear while you make an oral present-ation on Mardi Gras.

Postcard Projects: Creative Ideas for Studying Our 50 States © 1995 Good Apple

LOUISIANA

The Battle of New Orleans was fought after the War of 1812 ended. Find out about the Battle of New Orleans. Why did it happen? Do you think it could happen today? Explain your answers using complete sentences.

Postcard Projects: Creative Ideas for Studying Our 50 States © 1995 Good Apple

LOUISIANA

Capital – **Augusta**

Size – **30,995 square miles**
(rank: 39)

Statehood – **March 15, 1820**
(23rd state)

Song – **"State of Maine Song"**

Bird – **Chickadee**

Flower – **White pine cone**
and tassel

Tree – **Eastern white pine**

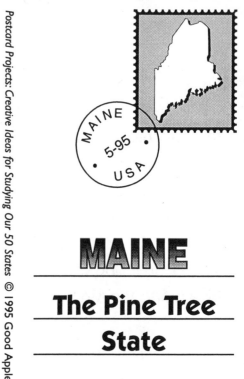

Postcard Projects: Creative Ideas for Studying Our 50 States © 1995 Good Apple

MAINE

The Pine Tree
State

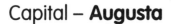he Maine Indian Claims Settlement Act was signed by President Carter in 1980. What tribes were involved? What was their claim? How was it settled? Write an editorial answering these questions and stating your opinion of the act.

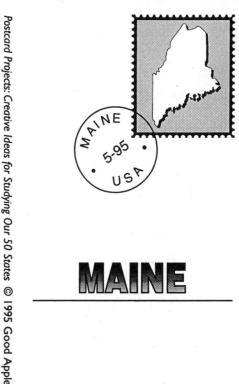

Postcard Projects: Creative Ideas for Studying Our 50 States © 1995 Good Apple

MAINE

Maine lobsters are a favorite seafood. Why are lobsters from Maine famous? Make a poster showing the life cycle of a lobster. Include information telling why lobsters thrive along the Maine coast.

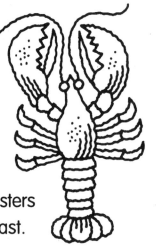

Postcard Projects: Creative Ideas for Studying Our 50 States © 1995 Good Apple

MAINE

Hansen Gregory invented the donut hole. Interview a baker to find out what his or her life is like including such information as what donuts are the most or least popular. Prepare a presentation of the information you have gathered.

Postcard Projects: Creative Ideas for Studying Our 50 States © 1995 Good Apple

MAINE

Maine is a beautiful state. There are many things to see and do. Read about Maine and write a cinquain poem about the state.

Postcard Projects: Creative Ideas for Studying Our 50 States © 1995 Good Apple

MAINE 5-95 USA

MAINE

When visiting the coast of Maine during the summer, windjammers can be seen sailing the waters. Illustrate a windjammer on a poster and label its parts.

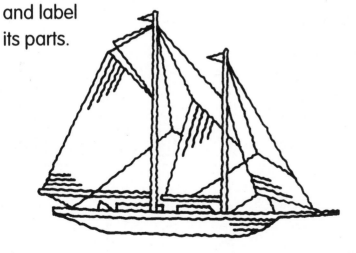

Postcard Projects: Creative Ideas for Studying Our 50 States © 1995 Good Apple

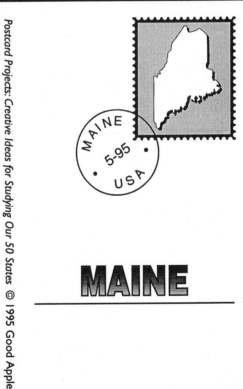

MAINE 5-95 USA

MAINE

Capital – **Annapolis**

Size – **9,838 square miles**
(rank: 42)

Statehood – **April 28, 1788**
(7th state)

Song – **"Maryland, My Maryland"**

Bird – **Baltimore oriole**

Flower – **Black-eyed Susan**

Tree – **White oak**

Postcard Projects: Creative Ideas for Studying Our 50 States © 1995 Good Apple

MARYLAND

The Old Line State

Our National Anthem, "The Star-Spangled Banner," was written by Francis Scott Key after a battle over Fort McHenry. Write a story about this famous battle.

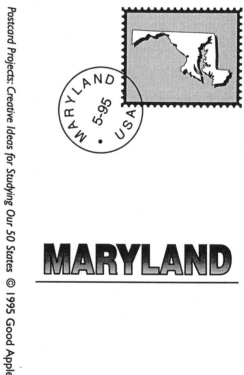

Postcard Projects: Creative Ideas for Studying Our 50 States © 1995 Good Apple

MARYLAND

In Baltimore, Maryland, you can visit the U.S. Frigate Constellation, the oldest United States Navy ship afloat. Make a poster of the ship and compare it to the ships of today.

Postcard Projects: Creative Ideas for Studying Our 50 States © 1995 Good Apple

MARYLAND

Camp David, the President's retreat, is located in Maryland. Find out about its history and what it looks like. Write a story or report describing what you found.

Postcard Projects: Creative Ideas for Studying Our 50 States © 1995 Good Apple

MARYLAND

Annapolis is the home of the United States Naval Academy. Write to your Naval recruiting office requesting information about the Naval Academy. In your letter include questions you would like to have answered.

Postcard Projects: Creative Ideas for Studying Our 50 States © 1995 Good Apple

MARYLAND
5-95
USA

MARYLAND

Clara Barton, founder of the Red Cross, lived in Glen Echo, Maryland. Call or write your closest Red Cross office and find out what the Red Cross does today. Create an illustrated brochure telling about services the Red Cross offers.

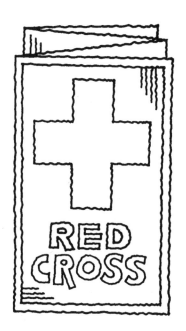

RED CROSS

Postcard Projects: Creative Ideas for Studying Our 50 States © 1995 Good Apple

MARYLAND
5-95
USA

MARYLAND

Capital – **Boston**

Size – **7,826 square miles
(rank: 45)**

Statehood – **February 6, 1788
(6th state)**

Song – **"All Hail
to Massachusetts"**

Bird – **Chickadee**

Flower – **Mayflower**

Tree – **Elm**

Postcard Projects: Creative Ideas for Studying Our 50 States © 1995 Good Apple

MASSACHUSETTS

The Bay

State

The Oceanographic Institution is located in Woods Hole on Cape Cod. Research some information about the life and contributions of one famous ocean-ographer. Make a mobile that high-lights what you learned.

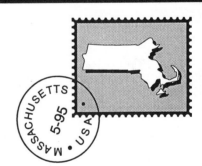

Postcard Projects: Creative Ideas for Studying Our 50 States © 1995 Good Apple

MASSACHUSETTS

South of Cape Cod is the island of Nantucket which became famous during the days of the whaling trade. Imagine you were an old-time whaler and write a story about one of your hunts.

Postcard Projects: Creative Ideas for Studying Our 50 States © 1995 Good Apple

MASSACHUSETTS

The Berkshire Hills are in the highlands of western Massachusetts. The hills are part of the Appalachian system and a continuation of the Green Mountains of Vermont. Pretend you are on a trip through the Berkshire Hills. Write a diary describing your experience.

DIARY
THE BERKSHIRE HILLS

Postcard Projects: Creative Ideas for Studying Our 50 States © 1995 Good Apple

MASSACHUSETTS

John F. Kennedy, our 35th president, was assassinated in 1963. His brother Robert was slain in 1968 while campaigning for the presidency. Find out about the Kennedy family and make a family tree.

Postcard Projects: Creative Ideas for Studying Our 50 States © 1995 Good Apple

MASSACHUSETTS

Boston, the capital of Massachusetts and a major seaport, played an important role in the history of Colonial America. Make a time line beginning with Plymouth colony and ending in 1776 showing some of the events in the history of Massachusetts.

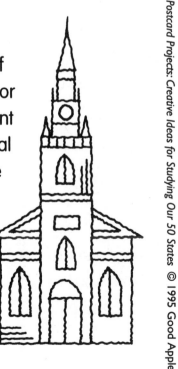

Postcard Projects: Creative Ideas for Studying Our 50 States © 1995 Good Apple

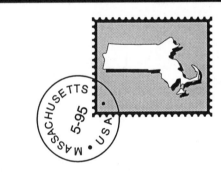

MASSACHUSETTS

Capital – **Lansing**

Size – **56,959 square miles**
(rank: 22)

Statehood – **January 26, 1837**
(26th state)

Song – **"Michigan, My Michigan"**

Bird – **Robin**

Flower – **Apple blossom**

Tree – **White pine**

Postcard Projects: Creative Ideas for Studying Our 50 States © 1995 Good Apple

MICHIGAN

The Great
Lake State

The Upper Peninsula of Michigan is noted for its wilderness and natural beauty. Read about this area. Choose a place you would like

to camp for one week. Write a description of the camp site you choose and make a list of all the supplies and equipment you and a friend will need for the week.

Postcard Projects: Creative Ideas for Studying Our 50 States © 1995 Good Apple

MICHIGAN

Battle Creek is the home of Kellogg's cereals. Choose five Kellogg's cereals and look at the nutritional information on the side of the boxes. Make a chart comparing this information.

Postcard Projects: Creative Ideas for Studying Our 50 States © 1995 Good Apple

MICHIGAN

Detroit is famous for automobile manufacturing. Find out some information about this manufacturing center. Illustrate and describe some of the processes used to build cars.

Postcard Projects: Creative Ideas for Studying Our 50 States © 1995 Good Apple

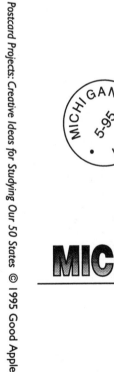

MICHIGAN

The state of Michigan touches four of the five Great Lakes. Find out about these four Great Lakes. Draw a poster (divided into four sections) that highlights each of the lakes. Include a description of the environmental conditions of these lakes.

Postcard Projects: Creative Ideas for Studying Our 50 States © 1995 Good Apple

MICHIGAN

Ralph Bunche, born in Detroit, was the first African American to win a Nobel Peace Prize. Read about his life and give a first person oral presentation to the class.

Postcard Projects: Creative Ideas for Studying Our 50 States © 1995 Good Apple

MICHIGAN

Capital – **St. Paul**

Size – **79,548 square miles**
(rank: 14)

Statehood – **May 11, 1858**
(32nd state)

Song – **"Hail! Minnesota"**

Bird – **Common loon**

Flower – **Pink-and-white**
lady's slipper

Tree – **Red pine**

Postcard Projects: Creative Ideas for Studying Our 50 States © 1995 Good Apple

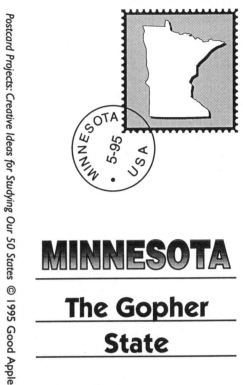

MINNESOTA

The Gopher
State

In 1832, Henry Schoolcraft discovered the source of the Mississippi River. Make a topographical map of Minnesota showing where the river starts.

Postcard Projects: Creative Ideas for Studying Our 50 States © 1995 Good Apple

MINNESOTA

The Mayo Clinic is located in Rochester, Minnesota. Read about the Mayo family and the clinic. Make a chart listing some of the

important contributions the Mayo family and clinic have made to the field of medicine.

Postcard Projects: Creative Ideas for Studying Our 50 States © 1995 Good Apple

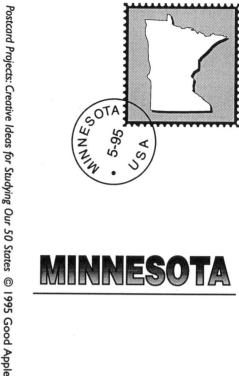

MINNESOTA

Minnesota has extensive national parks and forests. Make a map of Minnesota showing where these parks and forests are located. Label each one and include its size.

Postcard Projects: Creative Ideas for Studying Our 50 States © 1995 Good Apple

MINNESOTA

Each year the walleye, walleyed pike, and muskies draw fisherman to Minnesota, the land of 10,000 lakes. Make an illustration of each of these fish and describe the environment in which each fish lives.

Postcard Projects: Creative Ideas for Studying Our 50 States © 1995 Good Apple

MINNESOTA 5-95 USA

MINNESOTA

Tales of Paul Bunyan and his big blue ox, Babe, are part of Minnesota's lore. Read a story about Paul Bunyan and then write an original tale of your own about him.

Postcard Projects: Creative Ideas for Studying Our 50 States © 1995 Good Apple

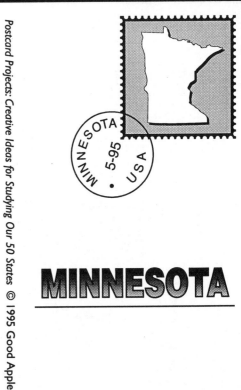

MINNESOTA 5-95 USA

MINNESOTA

Capital – **Jackson**

Size – **47,234 square miles (rank: 31)**

Statehood – **December 10, 1817 (20th state)**

Song – **"Go, Mississippi"**

Bird – **Mockingbird**

Flower – **Magnolia**

Tree – **Southern magnolia**

Postcard Projects: Creative Ideas for Studying Our 50 States © 1995 Good Apple

MISSISSIPPI

The Magnolia State

In 1798, Congress organized the Mississippi Territory. Winthrop Sargent was its first governor. Make a map of the territory as it was in 1798 and a map of the state as it is today. Describe the differences in a short paragraph.

Postcard Projects: Creative Ideas for Studying Our 50 States © 1995 Good Apple

MISSISSIPPI

The Old Capitol is located in Jackson, Mississippi. This building houses the State Historical Museum and is an excellent example of Greek Revival architecture. On a poster, illustrate this style of architecture and write the names of other famous buildings that are examples of the Greek Revival style.

Postcard Projects: Creative Ideas for Studying Our 50 States © 1995 Good Apple

MISSISSIPPI

Magnolias, camellias, and azaleas grow in beautiful abundance in Mississippi. Make a detailed color illustration of each flower and explain in a paragraph why Mississippi provides such perfect conditions for flowers to grow.

Postcard Projects: Creative Ideas for Studying Our 50 States © 1995 Good Apple

MISSISSIPPI

William Faulkner was born in New Albany, Mississippi and won the Pulitzer Prize for literature in 1955 and 1963. Which of his books were awarded the Pulitzer Prize? What kind of life did he have? Design a bookmark that explains the answers to these questions.

Postcard Projects: Creative Ideas for Studying Our 50 States © 1995 Good Apple

MISSISSIPPI

The Mississippi River, flowing 2,340 miles, is the longest river in the United States. Explorers and tradesmen have relied on the river and sternwheel riverboats still ply its waters. Find a recording of the song "Ol' Man River" by Jerome Kern and Oscar Hammerstein II. Play it for the class and analyze the lyrics as they portrayed life on the Mississippi.

Postcard Projects: Creative Ideas for Studying Our 50 States © 1995 Good Apple

MISSISSIPPI

Capital – **Jefferson City**

Size – **68,945 square miles (rank: 18)**

Statehood – **August 10, 1821 (24th state)**

Song – **"Missouri Waltz"**

Bird – **Bluebird**

Flower – **Hawthorn**

Tree – **Dogwood**

Postcard Projects: Creative Ideas for Studying Our 50 States © 1995 Good Apple

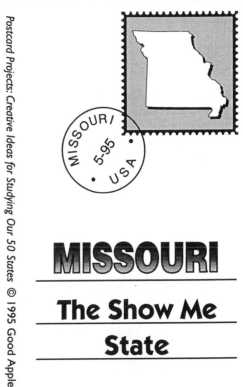

MISSOURI

The Show Me State

St. Louis is full of exciting places to visit. While there, vacationers can see the St. Louis Zoo, Missouri Botanical Garden, and Jewel Box. Find out about the Jewel Box and design a postage stamp to commemorate this beautiful site.

Postcard Projects: Creative Ideas for Studying Our 50 States © 1995 Good Apple

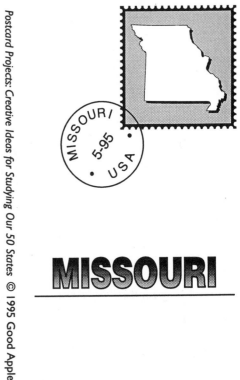

MISSOURI

Paddle wheel steamboats, which had a great influence on the region and people in Missouri for about fifty years, went up and down the Mississippi River between St. Louis and New Orleans. Pretend you just traveled the Mississippi in a steamboat. Write a story about the trip including as many facts as possible.

Postcard Projects: Creative Ideas for Studying Our 50 States © 1995 Good Apple

MISSOURI 5-95 USA

MISSOURI

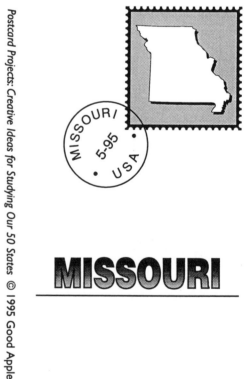

The Gateway Arch in St. Louis is a famous landmark. Read about the Gateway Arch and design a travel brochure for tourists.

Postcard Projects: Creative Ideas for Studying Our 50 States © 1995 Good Apple

MISSOURI 5-95 USA

MISSOURI

Find out why Charles A. Lindbergh and the Spirit of St. Louis are famous. Write a story as it might have appeared in a newspaper explaining their notoriety.

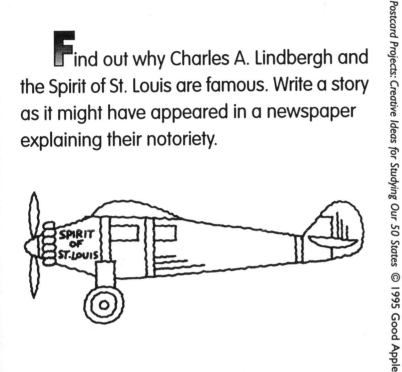

Postcard Projects: Creative Ideas for Studying Our 50 States © 1995 Good Apple

MISSOURI 5-95 USA

MISSOURI

Samuel Clemens, who is also known as Mark Twain, grew up in Hannibal, Missouri on the Mississippi River. Make a storyboard about Samuel Clemens' life in Hannibal and how it influenced his writing.

Postcard Projects: Creative Ideas for Studying Our 50 States © 1995 Good Apple

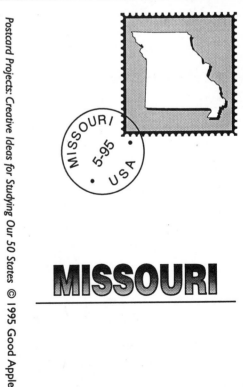

MISSOURI 5-95 USA

MISSOURI

Capital – **Helena**

Size – **145,388 square miles (rank: 4)**

Statehood – **November 8, 1889 (41st state)**

Song – **"Montana"**

Bird – **Western meadowlark**

Flower – **Bitterroot**

Tree – **Ponderosa pine**

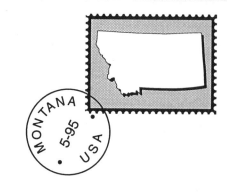

Postcard Projects: Creative Ideas for Studying Our 50 States © 1995 Good Apple

MONTANA

The Treasure State

Glacier National Park is along Montana's northern border and extends into Canada. Read about glaciers. Make a map of the world showing where glaciers are located. On your map, write a short description about glaciers including what they are and how they are formed.

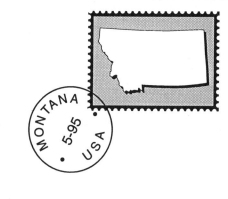

Postcard Projects: Creative Ideas for Studying Our 50 States © 1995 Good Apple

MONTANA

The Continental Divide runs through Montana. Research what it might have been like for the early settlers moving west to cross the Continental Divide. Pretend you are one of the settlers and write a diary of your journey over a two-week period.

Postcard Projects: Creative Ideas for Studying Our 50 States © 1995 Good Apple

MONTANA

5-95

USA

MONTANA

Livestock production is an important industry in Montana. Find out about Richard Grant and Nelson Story and the beginning of the cattle industry in Montana. Using the information you found, create a cartoon with captions.

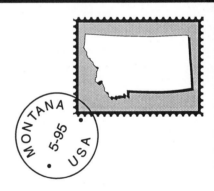

Postcard Projects: Creative Ideas for Studying Our 50 States © 1995 Good Apple

MONTANA

5-95

USA

MONTANA

Custer's Last Stand is a famous or infamous battle that took place on June 24, 1876. Read about this battle and write an essay telling whether you think it should be considered famous or infamous.

Postcard Projects: Creative Ideas for Studying Our 50 States © 1995 Good Apple

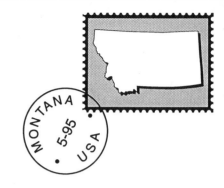

MONTANA

Montana is practically unequaled when it comes to outdoor recreation opportunities. Make a poster illustrating and describing the many varied outdoor attractions in Montana.

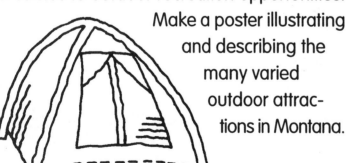

Postcard Projects: Creative Ideas for Studying Our 50 States © 1995 Good Apple

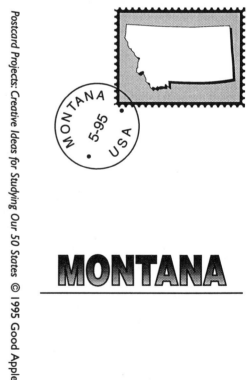

MONTANA

Capital – **Lincoln**

Size – **76,639 square miles**
(rank: 15)

Statehood – **March 1, 1867**
(37th state)

Song – **"Beautiful Nebraska"**

Bird – **Western meadowlark**

Flower – **Goldenrod**

Tree – **Cottonwood**

Postcard Projects: Creative Ideas for Studying Our 50 States © 1995 Good Apple

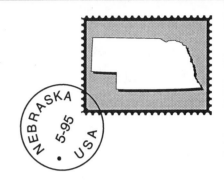

NEBRASKA

The Cornhusker State

Nebraska has seven state parks. Write to the director of the Game and Park Commission, Box 30370, Lincoln, NE 68509 for information. Design a newspaper ad encouraging travelers to visit Nebraska's parks.

Postcard Projects: Creative Ideas for Studying Our 50 States © 1995 Good Apple

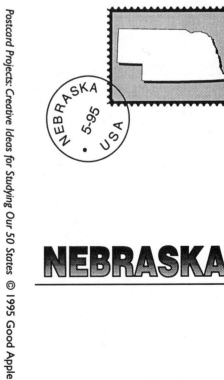

NEBRASKA

Red Cloud was home to Willa Cather who wrote about life in early Nebraska. Find out about her life and write a short biography.

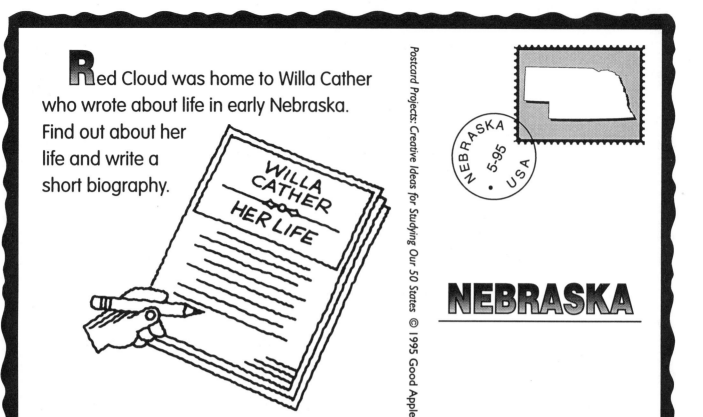

Postcard Projects: Creative Ideas for Studying Our 50 States © 1995 Good Apple

NEBRASKA
5-95
USA

NEBRASKA

Agate Fossil Beds National Monument near Scottsbluff contains fossils of animals that lived millions of years ago. Find out what kinds of animals lived in Nebraska and what the environment was like at that time. Make a diorama showing what you learned.

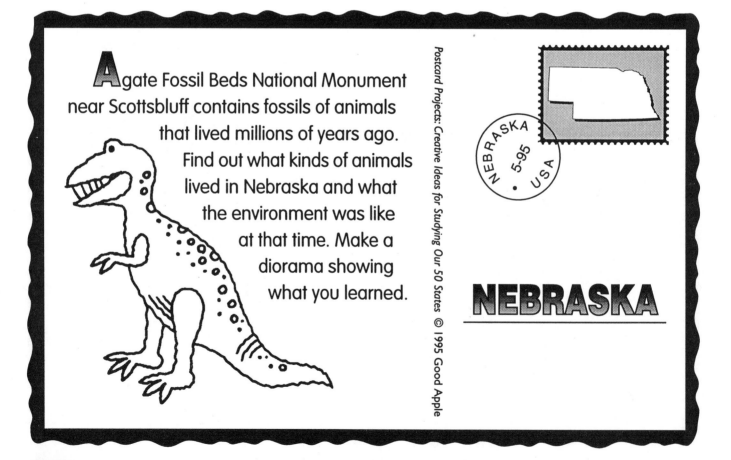

Postcard Projects: Creative Ideas for Studying Our 50 States © 1995 Good Apple

NEBRASKA
5-95
USA

NEBRASKA

In 1863, the Union Pacific Railroad broke ground in Omaha to begin joining the east coast with the west coast. Read about the construction of these rails and make a time line showing how it progressed.

Postcard Projects: Creative Ideas for Studying Our 50 States © 1995 Good Apple

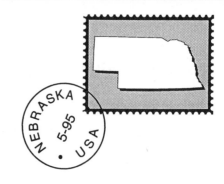

NEBRASKA

Nebraska was known as the corridor to the West. The Mormon Trail, the Oregon Trail, the Lewis and Clark Trail, and the Pony Express all went through Nebraska. Find out about these trails including why they went through Nebraska. Make a map of Nebraska and indicate where these trails were located.

Postcard Projects: Creative Ideas for Studying Our 50 States © 1995 Good Apple

NEBRASKA

Capital – **Carson City**

Size – **109,895 square miles (rank: 7)**

Statehood – **October 31, 1864 (36th state)**

Song – **"Home Means Nevada"**

Bird – **Mountain bluebird**

Flower – **Sagebrush**

Tree – **Single leaf pinon**

Postcard Projects: Creative Ideas for Studying Our 50 States © 1995 Good Apple

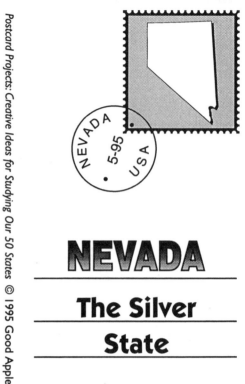

NEVADA

The Silver State

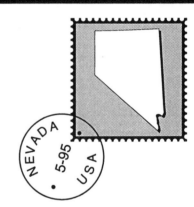

Gambling is a mainstay of Nevada's economy as demonstrated by the hundreds of people who visit the casinos each year. Write an editorial for or against legalizing gambling in your state.

Postcard Projects: Creative Ideas for Studying Our 50 States © 1995 Good Apple

NEVADA

The Comstock Lode was discovered in 1869. Read about the Comstock Lode and make a comic strip about life during that time.

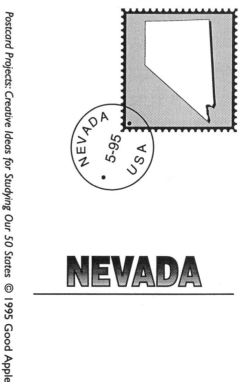

Postcard Projects: Creative Ideas for Studying Our 50 States © 1995 Good Apple

NEVADA

Many important events occurred in the history of Nevada. One such event was when Peter S. Ogden explored the Humboldt River Valley in 1825. Make a time line of Nevada's history starting in 1825 and continuing until 1936 when Hoover Dam was completed.

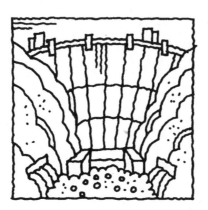

Postcard Projects: Creative Ideas for Studying Our 50 States © 1995 Good Apple

NEVADA

Carson City is named after Kit Carson. Find out about Kit Carson and write a poem about this fascinating American.

Postcard Projects: Creative Ideas for Studying Our 50 States © 1995 Good Apple

NEVADA 5-95 USA

NEVADA

A deposit of fossilized ichthyosaur bones is found at Ichthyosaur Paleontologic State Monument is central Nevada. Write and illustrate a children's story about an ichthyosaur.

Postcard Projects: Creative Ideas for Studying Our 50 States © 1995 Good Apple

NEVADA 5-95 USA

NEVADA

Capital – **Concord**

Size – **8,992 square miles**
(rank: 44)

Statehood – **June 21, 1788**
(9th state)

Song – **"Old New Hampshire"**

Bird – **Purple finch**

Flower – **Purple lilac**

Tree – **White birch**

Postcard Projects: Creative Ideas for Studying Our 50 States © 1995 Good Apple

NEW HAMPSHIRE
The Granite State

The "Great Stone Face" of the Old Man of the Mountains is an important landmark in New Hampshire. Make a diorama of the Great Stone Face.

Postcard Projects: Creative Ideas for Studying Our 50 States © 1995 Good Apple

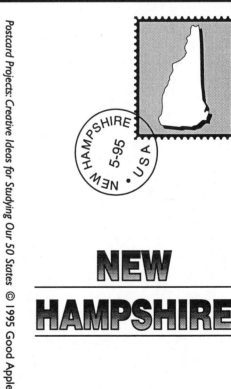

NEW HAMPSHIRE

The state's first cotton mill was founded at New Ipswich. Find out some important facts about cotton and make a list to record them. Design an illustrated chart showing the many uses for cotton.

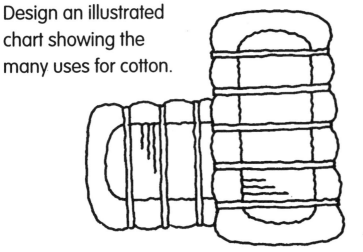

Postcard Projects: Creative Ideas for Studying Our 50 States © 1995 Good Apple

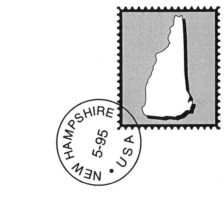

NEW HAMPSHIRE

Peterborough is in the heart of the Monadnock area and is known nationally as the home of the MacDowell Colony — a sanctuary for artists, writers, and musicians. Listen to a recording of a composition by Edward MacDowell and create an original illustration to go with it.

Postcard Projects: Creative Ideas for Studying Our 50 States © 1995 Good Apple

NEW HAMPSHIRE

Strawberry Bank is a restored colonial seaport in Portsmouth. Find out about colonial seaports. Then draw the types of items or scenes you might have seen there.

Postcard Projects: Creative Ideas for Studying Our 50 States © 1995 Good Apple

NEW HAMPSHIRE

Daniel Webster, whose home is near Franklin, argued for the trustees in the case of Dartmouth College v. Woodward (1819). This case was heard by the U. S. Supreme Court. Read about the U. S. Supreme Court and make a chart containing the names of today's chief justice and associate justices, as well as other pertinent information about them.

Postcard Projects: Creative Ideas for Studying Our 50 States © 1995 Good Apple

NEW HAMPSHIRE

Capital – **Trenton**

Size – **7,468 square miles (rank: 46)**

Statehood – **December 18, 1787 (3rd state)**

Song – **None**

Bird – **Eastern goldfinch**

Flower – **Purple violet**

Tree – **Red oak**

Postcard Projects: Creative Ideas for Studying Our 50 States © 1995 Good Apple

NEW JERSEY

The Garden State

In 1933, the first drive-in movie theater was opened in New Jersey. The idea spread across the United States, and soon drive-ins were found in many towns. Today, very few are left. Write an editorial telling why you think drive-in movies died out and why they should or should not be revived.

Postcard Projects: Creative Ideas for Studying Our 50 States © 1995 Good Apple

NEW JERSEY

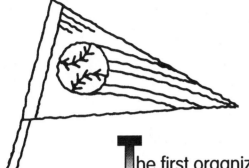

Postcard Projects: Creative Ideas for Studying Our 50 States © 1995 Good Apple

NEW JERSEY

The first organized baseball game was played on the Elysian Fields in Hoboken in 1845. Find out which teams played in that game. Design a pennant and logo for each team. Then find out how the rules of baseball have changed since 1845.

Postcard Projects: Creative Ideas for Studying Our 50 States © 1995 Good Apple

NEW JERSEY

In 1804 at Weehawken, Aaron Burr and Alexander Hamilton fought a famous duel. Write a television news report about the duel.

Cape May, on the popular Jersey shore, is the oldest resort in the United States. It is known for its over 200 beautifully restored Victorian homes. Do some research on Victorian architecture and find out what makes it unique. Prepare a photo display of Victorian buildings or design a Victorian home.

Postcard Projects: Creative Ideas for Studying Our 50 States © 1995 Good Apple

NEW JERSEY

Thomas Edison, the "Wizard of Menlo Park," is one of the United States' most famous inventors. On a chart, list several of Edison's inventions and show how they have developed into items we have today. For example, trace Edison's phonograph to compact disc players.

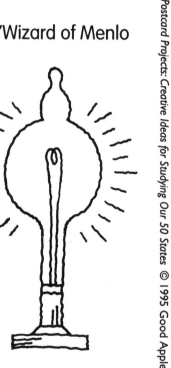

Postcard Projects: Creative Ideas for Studying Our 50 States © 1995 Good Apple

NEW JERSEY

Capital – **Santa Fe**

Size – **121,336 square miles
(rank: 5)**

Statehood – **January 6, 1912
(47th state)**

Song – **"Asi es Nuevo Mexico" and
"O, Fair New Mexico"**

Bird – **Roadrunner**

Flower – **Yucca**

Tree – **Pinon**

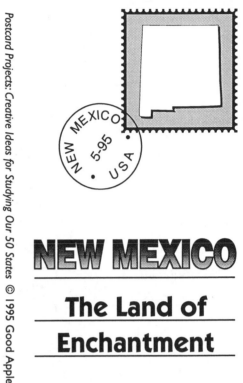

Postcard Projects: Creative Ideas for Studying Our 50 States © 1995 Good Apple

NEW MEXICO

The Land of
Enchantment

Many of the buildings in New Mexico are made of adobe. Find out about adobe and construct a model of an adobe building using clay.

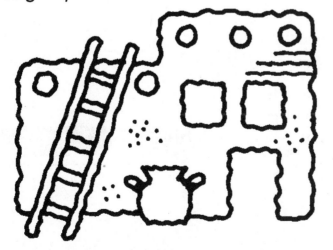

Postcard Projects: Creative Ideas for Studying Our 50 States © 1995 Good Apple

NEW MEXICO

New Mexico has a colorful and exciting history. Make a time line of the state's history beginning with 1540 when Coronado explored the region and ending with New Mexico's statehood.

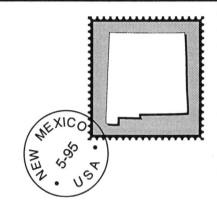

Postcard Projects: Creative Ideas for Studying Our 50 States © 1995 Good Apple

NEW MEXICO

In 1950, Paddy Martinez discovered uranium in New Mexico. Investigate the importance and uses of uranium. Make an illustrated chart showing what you discovered.

Postcard Projects: Creative Ideas for Studying Our 50 States © 1995 Good Apple

NEW MEXICO

Pueblos are located near Santa Fe. Read about the Native Americans who lived in these Pueblos. Make a diorama to show what a pueblo looks like.

Postcard Projects: Creative Ideas for Studying Our 50 States © 1995 Good Apple

NEW MEXICO

Billy the Kid, the notorious outlaw, has become a part of America's folklore. Make a "Wanted" poster about Billy the Kid.

Postcard Projects: Creative Ideas for Studying Our 50 States © 1995 Good Apple

NEW MEXICO

Capital – **Albany**

Size – **47,379 square miles**
(rank: 30)

Statehood – **July 26, 1788**
(11th state)

Song – **"I Love New York"**

Bird – **Bluebird**

Flower – **Rose**

Tree – **Sugar maple**

Postcard Projects: Creative Ideas for Studying Our 50 States © 1995 Good Apple

NEW YORK

5-95

USA

NEW YORK

The Empire State

The Hudson River Valley, named after Henry Hudson, is the setting for Washington Irving's stories, "The Legend of Sleepy Hollow" and "Rip Van Winkle." Read one of these stories and make a storyboard depicting an important scene.

Postcard Projects: Creative Ideas for Studying Our 50 States © 1995 Good Apple

NEW YORK

5-95

USA

NEW YORK

On the North Shore of Long Island is Sagamore Hill, the summer home of Theodore Roosevelt. Make a time line of the life of this famous president.

Postcard Projects: Creative Ideas for Studying Our 50 States © 1995 Good Apple

NEW YORK

The Statue of Liberty stands at the entrance to New York Harbor, where it has welcomed travelers and immigrants for over one hundred years. Pretend you are arriving in the United States as an immigrant in the early 1900's. Write a poem describing your feelings as you see "Lady Liberty" for the first time.

Postcard Projects: Creative Ideas for Studying Our 50 States © 1995 Good Apple

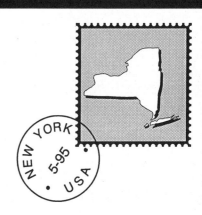

NEW YORK

The little town of Cooperstown houses the Baseball Hall of Fame and is an intriguing place to visit. Find out about the many things to see and do in Cooperstown. Choose the one that appeals to you the most and design a one-page magazine ad about it.

Postcard Projects: Creative Ideas for Studying Our 50 States © 1995 Good Apple

NEW YORK

The Catskill Mountains are famous for their many resorts. Plan a family vacation to this area. Describe where you will go, what you will see, and what you will do. Make a drawing of one part of your trip.

Postcard Projects: Creative Ideas for Studying Our 50 States © 1995 Good Apple

NEW YORK

Capital – **Raleigh**

Size – **48,843 square miles**
(rank: 29)

Statehood – **November 21, 1789**
(12th state)

Song – **"The Old North State"**

Bird – **Cardinal**

Flower – **Dogwood**

Tree – **Long leaf pine**

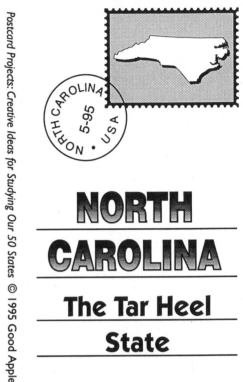

Postcard Projects: Creative Ideas for Studying Our 50 States © 1995 Good Apple

NORTH CAROLINA
The Tar Heel State

The tallest lighthouse in the United States is located at Cape Hatteras in North Carolina, the "Graveyard of the Atlantic." This lighthouse protects ships from the treacherous Diamond Shoals. Make a mural illustrating this lighthouse and describe why the Diamond Shoals can be so dangerous.

Postcard Projects: Creative Ideas for Studying Our 50 States © 1995 Good Apple

NORTH CAROLINA

The Outer Banks form a unique environment along the North Carolina coast. Design a postcard depicting the Outer Banks. Include a message describing the area.

Postcard Projects: Creative Ideas for Studying Our 50 States © 1995 Good Apple

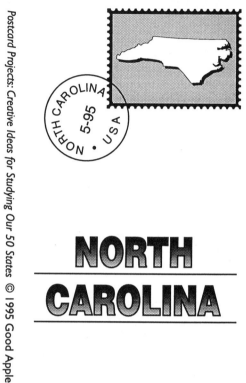

NORTH CAROLINA

North Carolina's capital, Raleigh, is named after Sir Walter Raleigh. Read about Sir Walter Raleigh. Make a diorama illustrating his life and role in the history of North Carolina.

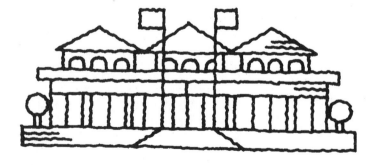

Postcard Projects: Creative Ideas for Studying Our 50 States © 1995 Good Apple

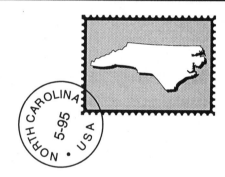

NORTH CAROLINA

The Biltmore House in Asheville is the largest family home in the United States. The estate was built to be self-sustaining. Find out what "self-sustaining" means. Then draw and label a map of the self-sustaining estate.

Postcard Projects: Creative Ideas for Studying Our 50 States © 1995 Good Apple

NORTH CAROLINA

Wilbur and Orville Wright flew the first successful airplane at Kitty Hawk in 1903. Build a model of the plane whose first flight carried Orville 120 feet and lasted 12 seconds.

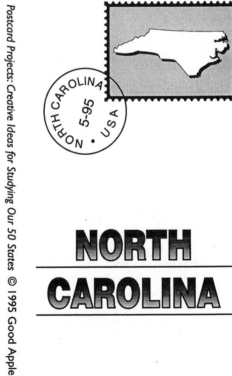

Postcard Projects: Creative Ideas for Studying Our 50 States © 1995 Good Apple

NORTH CAROLINA

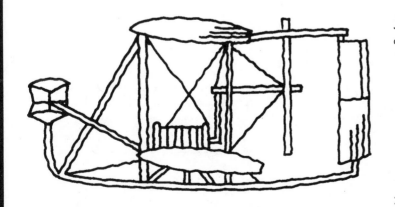

Capital – **Bismarck**

Size – **69,299 square miles
(rank: 17)**

Statehood – **November 2, 1889
(39th state)**

Song – **"North Dakota Hymn"**

Bird – **Western meadowlark**

Flower – **Wild prairie rose**

Tree – **American elm**

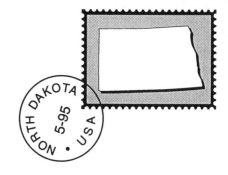

Postcard Projects: Creative Ideas for Studying Our 50 States © 1995 Good Apple

NORTH DAKOTA

**The Flickertail
State**

In 1863, the Dakota Territory was opened for homesteading. Find out about the early homesteaders and what they had to do to keep their land. Imagine you lived on a homestead. Write a journal describing your life.

Postcard Projects: Creative Ideas for Studying Our 50 States © 1995 Good Apple

NORTH DAKOTA

The Badlands are found in southwestern North Dakota. How did they get their name? What does this area look like? Share your research in an illustrated travel brochure.

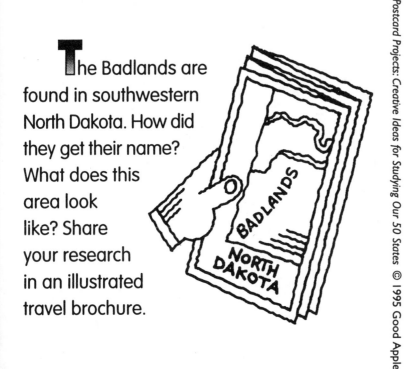

Postcard Projects: Creative Ideas for Studying Our 50 States © 1995 Good Apple

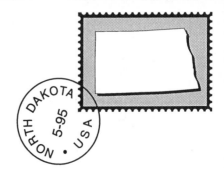

NORTH DAKOTA

North Dakota has five Indian reservations. Draw a map of the state and show where the five reservations are located.

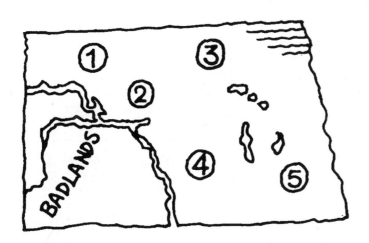

Postcard Projects: Creative Ideas for Studying Our 50 States © 1995 Good Apple

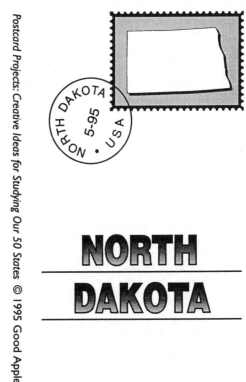

NORTH DAKOTA

"**P**rairie skyscrapers" are found statewide and are essential to the economic life of the state. Find out the function of these "skyscrapers." Make a model of a "skyscraper" and present an explanation of its importance.

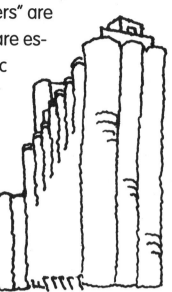

Postcard Projects: Creative Ideas for Studying Our 50 States © 1995 Good Apple

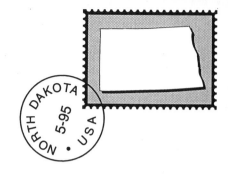

NORTH DAKOTA USA
5-95

NORTH DAKOTA

Fargo, the largest city in North Dakota, is named after William G. Fargo of Wells, Fargo and Company. The logo for Wells, Fargo and Company is a stagecoach. Read about William G. Fargo. Explain the significance of the stagecoach and design a new logo for the company.

Postcard Projects: Creative Ideas for Studying Our 50 States © 1995 Good Apple

NORTH DAKOTA USA
5-95

NORTH DAKOTA

Capital – **Columbus**

Size – **41,004 square miles**
(rank: 35)

Statehood – **March 1, 1803**
(17th state)

Song – **"Beautiful Ohio"**

Bird – **Cardinal**

Flower – **Scarlet carnation**

Tree – **Buckeye**

Postcard Projects: Creative Ideas for Studying Our 50 States © 1995 Good Apple

OHIO
5-95
USA

OHIO

The Buckeye
State

B.F. Goodrich began making rubber products in 1870 in Akron. Read about Goodrich and the production of rubber and make a flow chart showing how rubber is produced.

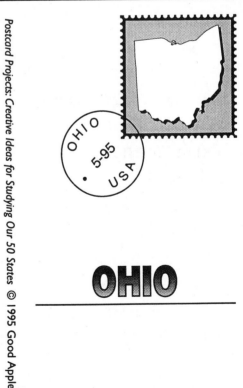

Postcard Projects: Creative Ideas for Studying Our 50 States © 1995 Good Apple

OHIO
5-95
USA

OHIO

In 1869, the Cincinnati Red Stockings became the first professional baseball team. Find out about the Red Stockings and design a pennant for the team. Include a logo on the pennant.

Postcard Projects: Creative Ideas for Studying Our 50 States © 1995 Good Apple

OHIO 5-95 USA

OHIO

_____

Ohio claims to be the "Mother of Presidents." Seven United States presidents were born there. Find out the names of those seven presidents, when they lived, and significant events in their presidency. Record what you find on a chart.

Postcard Projects: Creative Ideas for Studying Our 50 States © 1995 Good Apple

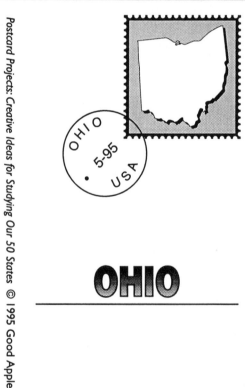

OHIO 5-95 USA

OHIO

_____

In 1813, Commodore Oliver H. Perry's fleet defeated the British in the Battle of Lake Erie. Research the kinds of war ships that were used in the 1830's and the kinds of war ships used today. Make a poster showing the evolution of war ships.

Postcard Projects: Creative Ideas for Studying Our 50 States © 1995 Good Apple

OHIO
5-95
USA

OHIO

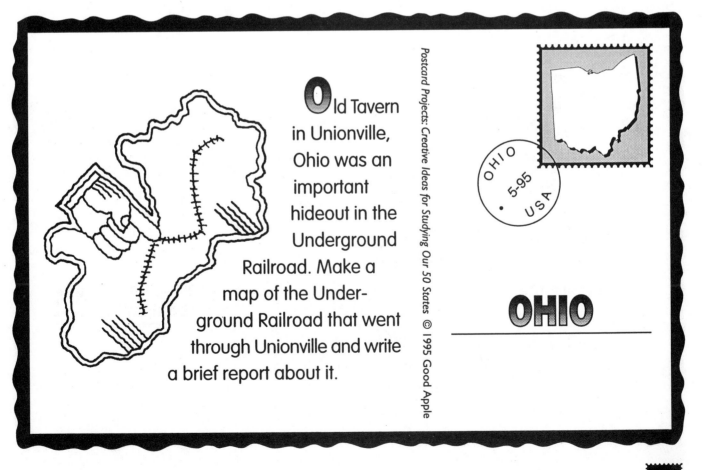

Old Tavern in Unionville, Ohio was an important hideout in the Underground Railroad. Make a map of the Underground Railroad that went through Unionville and write a brief report about it.

Postcard Projects: Creative Ideas for Studying Our 50 States © 1995 Good Apple

OHIO
5-95
USA

OHIO

Capital – **Oklahoma City**

Size – **68,656 square miles
(rank: 19)**

Statehood – **November 16, 1907
(46th state)**

Song – **"Oklahoma"**

Bird – **Scissor-tailed flycatcher**

Flower – **Mistletoe**

Tree – **Redbud**

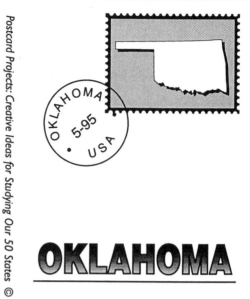

Postcard Projects: Creative Ideas for Studying Our 50 States © 1995 Good Apple

OKLAHOMA
The Sooner
State

The oil boom of the early 1920's caused great changes in Oklahoma. Read about this period and make a "before-and-after" chart to show the changes that took place.

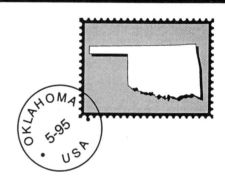

Postcard Projects: Creative Ideas for Studying Our 50 States © 1995 Good Apple

OKLAHOMA

Sequoyah devised an alphabet for the Cherokee language. Make a chart of the alphabet and give an oral presentation about Sequoyah.

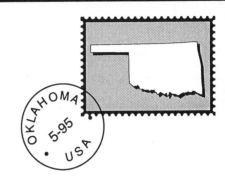

ALPHABET FOR THE CHEROKEE LANGUAGE

◆

SEQUOYAH

Postcard Projects: Creative Ideas for Studying Our 50 States © 1995 Good Apple

OKLAHOMA

Runestones found at Poteau Mountain are believed to have been left by Viking explorers. How did Vikings get to Oklahoma? Write a hypothesis to explain this. Be sure to include reasons to support this hypothesis.

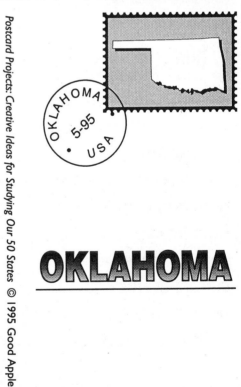

Postcard Projects: Creative Ideas for Studying Our 50 States © 1995 Good Apple

OKLAHOMA

The land rush of April 11, 1889 resulted in the settlement of northern Oklahoma. Make a map of the area and briefly describe what happened to the Native Americans in the area and what the government and the settlers were trying to achieve.

Postcard Projects: Creative Ideas for Studying Our 50 States © 1995 Good Apple

OKLAHOMA

OKLAHOMA 5-95 USA

Will Rogers of Oklahoma was a cowboy humorist famous for his amusingly shrewd observations on current events. He often chewed gum and performed rope tricks while he spoke. Choose a few current events and perform a Will Rogers-style lecture.

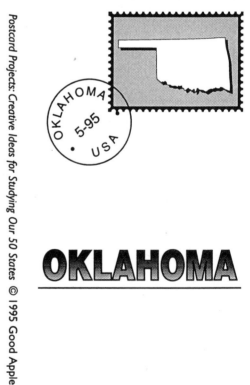

Postcard Projects: Creative Ideas for Studying Our 50 States © 1995 Good Apple

OKLAHOMA

OKLAHOMA 5-95 USA

Capital – **Salem**

Size – **96,187 square miles**
(rank: **10**)

Statehood – **February 14, 1859**
(**33rd state**)

Song – **"Oregon, My Oregon"**

Bird – **Western meadowlark**

Flower – **Oregon grape**

Tree – **Douglas fir**

Postcard Projects: Creative Ideas for Studying Our 50 States © 1995 Good Apple

OREGON 5-95 USA

OREGON

The Beaver
State

The Oregon Trail ended in the Willamette Valley. Why did so many people want to go there? What was it like? What is the Willamette Valley like today? Illustrate a poster of the Willamette Valley then and now.

Postcard Projects: Creative Ideas for Studying Our 50 States © 1995 Good Apple

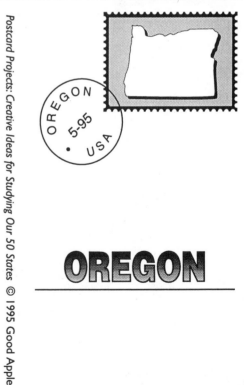

OREGON 5-95 USA

OREGON

Postcard Projects: Creative Ideas for Studying Our 50 States © 1995 Good Apple

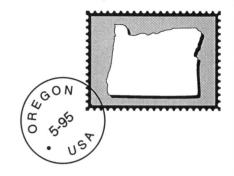

OREGON
5-95
USA

The Donation Land Law of 1850 spurred the settlement of Oregon. Find out about the provisions of the Donation Land Law. On a chart, list the provisions of the law and explain how it helped the settlement.

OREGON

Portland, Oregon is home to the world's smallest park — Mills End Park. Find out how and why the park was formed and write a story about it.

Postcard Projects: Creative Ideas for Studying Our 50 States © 1995 Good Apple

OREGON
5-95
USA

OREGON

John Jacob Astor founded Astoria, Oregon in 1811. Research Astor and his famous American family. Make a chart of their accomplishments.

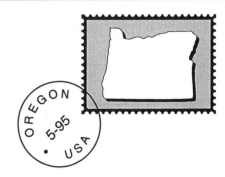

Postcard Projects: Creative Ideas for Studying Our 50 States © 1995 Good Apple

OREGON

OREGON 5-95 USA

Crater Lake National Park is Oregon's only national park. Find out how the lake was formed and what it looks like today. Write an illustrated report telling what you found.

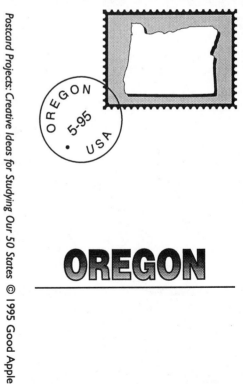

Postcard Projects: Creative Ideas for Studying Our 50 States © 1995 Good Apple

OREGON

OREGON 5-95 USA

Capital – **Harrisburg**

Size – **44,892 square miles (rank: 32)**

Statehood – **December 12, 1787 (2nd state)**

Song – **None**

Bird – **Ruffed grouse**

Flower – **Mountain laurel**

Tree – **Hemlock**

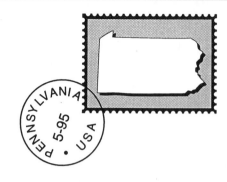

Postcard Projects: Creative Ideas for Studying Our 50 States © 1995 Good Apple

PENNSYLVANIA

The Keystone State

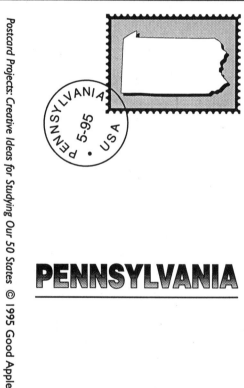

Hershey Chocolate Company, founded by Milton Hershey, is located in Hershey, Pennsylvania. Find out how chocolate candy is made. Design a flow chart to describe the process.

Postcard Projects: Creative Ideas for Studying Our 50 States © 1995 Good Apple

PENNSYLVANIA

The Pennsylvania Dutch actually came from Germany in the late 1600's and 1700's. They have a very distinct and colorful art style. Do some research on Pennsylvania Dutch art forms and create an original work of art in that style.

Postcard Projects: Creative Ideas for Studying Our 50 States © 1995 Good Apple

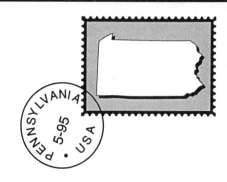

PENNSYLVANIA

Pennsylvania was founded by William Penn. Find out about him and the early settlement of Pennsylvania. Make a time line of Penn's life.

Postcard Projects: Creative Ideas for Studying Our 50 States © 1995 Good Apple

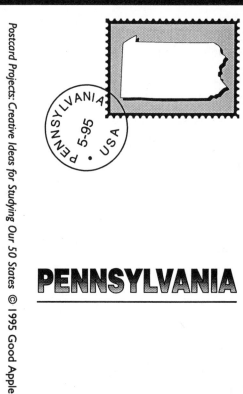

PENNSYLVANIA

On July 3, 1863, the Battle of Gettysburg was fought. Find out about this famous Civil War battle. Write a newspaper account (including a headline) of the battle.

Postcard Projects: Creative Ideas for Studying Our 50 States © 1995 Good Apple

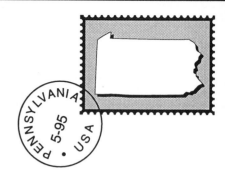

PENNSYLVANIA

Philadelphia owes much to Benjamin Franklin. Make a chart showing what his contributions were and when they were made.

Postcard Projects: Creative Ideas for Studying Our 50 States © 1995 Good Apple

PENNSYLVANIA

Capital – **Providence**

Size – **1,054 square miles**
(rank: 50)

Statehood – **May 29, 1790**
(13th state)

Song – **"Rhode Island"**

Bird – **Rhode Island red**

Flower – **Violet**

Tree – **Red maple**

Postcard Projects: Creative Ideas for Studying Our 50 States © 1995 Good Apple

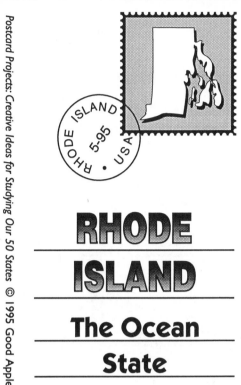

RHODE ISLAND 5-95 • USA

RHODE ISLAND

The Ocean State

The Dorr Rebellion in 1842 was an uprising to secure constitutional reform. Find out more about the Dorr Rebellion. How could the problems have been solved without an uprising? Write an editorial that could have provided the solutions.

Postcard Projects: Creative Ideas for Studying Our 50 States © 1995 Good Apple

RHODE ISLAND 5-95 • USA

RHODE ISLAND

Quonset Point Naval Air Station saw the development of the Quonset hut. Find out what a Quonset hut is and build a model.

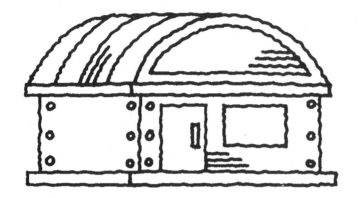

Postcard Projects: Creative Ideas for Studying Our 50 States © 1995 Good Apple

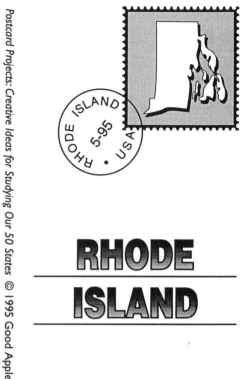

RHODE ISLAND _____ _____

Newport includes over 300 buildings from its colonial past as well as the beautiful "summer cottages" built by some of America's wealthiest families in the late 1800's. Research these "cottages" and choose one in which you'd like to live. Take the class on a narrated tour of your chosen home.

Postcard Projects: Creative Ideas for Studying Our 50 States © 1995 Good Apple

RHODE ISLAND _____ _____

Find out about Roger Williams and the founding of Rhode Island. Make a poster that could have been designed by Roger Williams to encourage others to settle in Rhode Island.

Postcard Projects: Creative Ideas for Studying Our 50 States © 1995 Good Apple

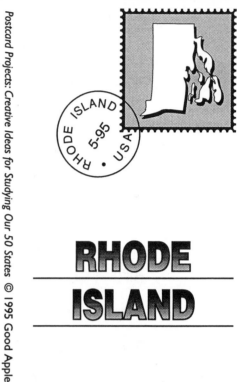

RHODE

ISLAND

The manufacturing of silverware and jewelry is important to Rhode Island's economy. Use modeling clay and paint to design a variety of jewelry pieces you believe would sell. Research the steps involved in transforming gold or silver into jewelry.

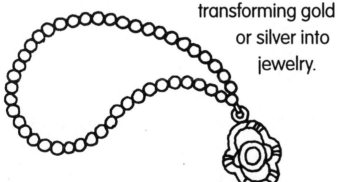

Postcard Projects: Creative Ideas for Studying Our 50 States © 1995 Good Apple

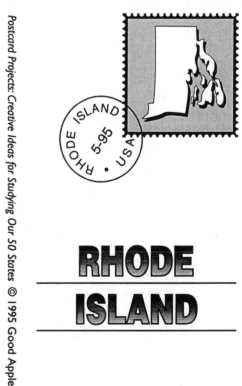

RHODE

ISLAND

Capital – **Columbia**

Size – **30,207 square miles**
(rank: 40)

Statehood – **May 23, 1788**
(8th state)

Song – **"South Carolina**
on My Mind"

Bird – **Carolina wren**

Flower – **Yellow jessamine**

Tree – **Palmetto**

Postcard Projects: Creative Ideas for Studying Our 50 States © 1995 Good Apple

SOUTH
CAROLINA
The Palmetto
State

Trumpet player Dizzy Gillespie, born in Cheraw, made enormous contributions to the world of jazz. Listen to some of Gillespie's recordings and select your favorite to share with the class.

Postcard Projects: Creative Ideas for Studying Our 50 States © 1995 Good Apple

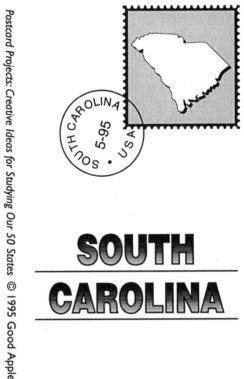

SOUTH
CAROLINA

The Civil War began in South Carolina with the shelling of Fort Sumter. Why did this happen? Create a political cartoon depicting this event.

Postcard Projects: Creative Ideas for Studying Our 50 States © 1995 Good Apple

SOUTH CAROLINA

The famous aircraft carrier of World War II, the Yorktown, is berthed at Patriot's Point. Find out how it got its nickname "Fighting Lady." Illustrate the different parts of an aircraft carrier and explain how a carrier operates.

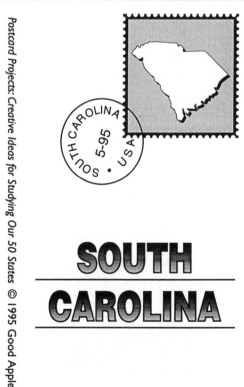

Postcard Projects: Creative Ideas for Studying Our 50 States © 1995 Good Apple

SOUTH CAROLINA

South Carolina is a popular vacation spot. Its sandy beaches, historic cities, and warm climate make tourism an important industry for the state. Make a travel brochure describing the many sites in South Carolina.

Postcard Projects: Creative Ideas for Studying Our 50 States © 1995 Good Apple

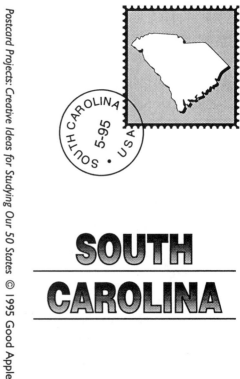

SOUTH CAROLINA

Beautiful landscaped gardens are a major tourist attraction in the Charleston area. Find out what plants and flowers are indigenous to South Carolina and design a garden people would enjoy walking through. Be sure to label everything.

Postcard Projects: Creative Ideas for Studying Our 50 States © 1995 Good Apple

SOUTH CAROLINA

Capital – **Pierre**

Size – **75,956 square miles
(rank: 16)**

Statehood – **November 2, 1889
(40th state)**

Song – **"Hail, South Dakota"**

Bird – **Ring-necked pheasant**

Flower – **American pasqueflower**

Tree – **Black Hills spruce**

Postcard Projects: Creative Ideas for Studying Our 50 States © 1995 Good Apple

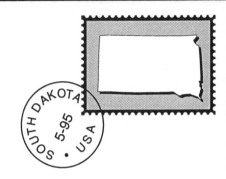

SOUTH DAKOTA
5-95
USA

SOUTH
DAKOTA

**The Sunshine
State**

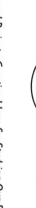eadwood City is located in the Black Hills. Read about this historic city of the old West and write a story that could have happened when "Calamity Jane" and "Wild Bill" Hickok lived there.

Postcard Projects: Creative Ideas for Studying Our 50 States © 1995 Good Apple

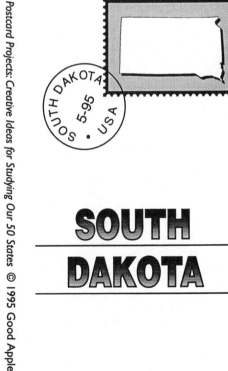

SOUTH DAKOTA
5-95
USA

SOUTH
DAKOTA

Mount Rushmore is a national monument located near Spearfish, South Dakota. On a large sheet of paper, draw Mount Rushmore and write a caption telling about it.

Postcard Projects: Creative Ideas for Studying Our 50 States © 1995 Good Apple

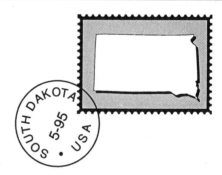

SOUTH DAKOTA • USA
5-95

SOUTH DAKOTA

DeSmet is the setting of Laura Ingalls Wilder's *Little Town on the Prairie, The Long Winter,* and *These Happy Golden Years.* Read one of these books and do some additional research in order to compare life in the country and life in the city. Record your findings in a Venn diagram.

THE LONG WINTER
LAURA INGALLS WILDER

Postcard Projects: Creative Ideas for Studying Our 50 States © 1995 Good Apple

SOUTH DAKOTA • USA
5-95

SOUTH DAKOTA

The oldest continuously operating gold mine is in South Dakota. Do some research to find out its name, location, and age. Use a Venn diagram to compare the gold mining process now to when the mine opened.

Postcard Projects: Creative Ideas for Studying Our 50 States © 1995 Good Apple

SOUTH DAKOTA • USA 5-95

SOUTH
DAKOTA

Mammoth Site at Hot Springs has one of the largest concentrations of mammoth skeletons in the world. Make a diorama depicting the area at the time of the mammoths.

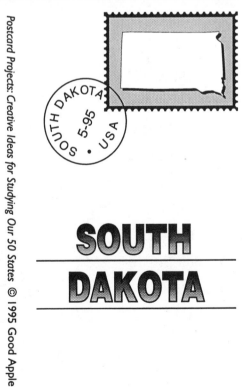

Postcard Projects: Creative Ideas for Studying Our 50 States © 1995 Good Apple

SOUTH DAKOTA • USA 5-95

SOUTH
DAKOTA

Capital – **Nashville**

Size – **41,154 square miles (rank: 34)**

Statehood – **June 1, 1796 (16th state)**

Song – **"The Tennessee Waltz" and four others**

Bird – **Mockingbird**

Flower – **Iris**

Tree – **Tulip poplar**

Postcard Projects: Creative Ideas for Studying Our 50 States © 1995 Good Apple

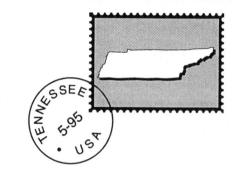

TENNESSEE

TENNESSEE
5-95
• USA

TENNESSEE

The Volunteer State

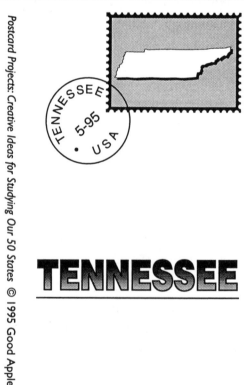

The home of "Casey Jones" is in Jackson. Read about this folk hero. Then write and illustrate a story telling about his heroic deed.

CASEY JONES

Postcard Projects: Creative Ideas for Studying Our 50 States © 1995 Good Apple

TENNESSEE
5-95
• USA

TENNESSEE

The TVA (Tennessee Valley Authority) began in 1933. Read about this agency and find out about TVA projects. Make a poster illustrating the various TVA projects. Under each illustration, write a brief description of the project. Be sure to include why the TVA was started.

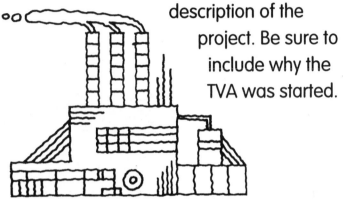

Postcard Projects: Creative Ideas for Studying Our 50 States © 1995 Good Apple

TENNESSEE 5-95 • USA

TENNESSEE

Three important Civil War battles were fought in Chattanooga. Read about each of these battles and make a chart comparing and contrasting the three battles.

Postcard Projects: Creative Ideas for Studying Our 50 States © 1995 Good Apple

TENNESSEE 5-95 • USA

TENNESSEE

Daniel Boone and Davy Crockett are both important historical figures in the state of Tennessee. Choose one and make a time line of his life.

Postcard Projects: Creative Ideas for Studying Our 50 States © 1995 Good Apple

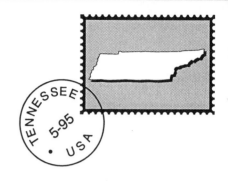

TENNESSEE

There are many interesting places to visit in Tennessee and many exciting things to do. On a large sheet of paper or poster board, draw the state of Tennessee including major cities, highways, lakes, and rivers. Below your drawing, write about places to see and things to do in this state. Make a creative map key to show where these places are.

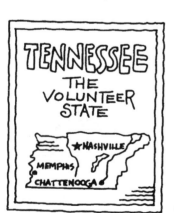

Postcard Projects: Creative Ideas for Studying Our 50 States © 1995 Good Apple

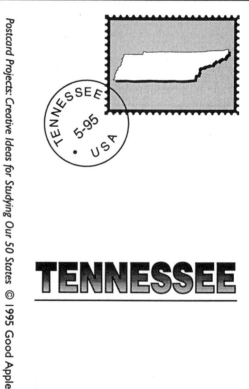

TENNESSEE

Capital – **Austin**

Size – **262,015 square miles
(rank: 2)**

Statehood – **December 29, 1845
(28th state)**

Song – **"Texas, Our Texas"**

Bird – **Mockingbird**

Flower – **Bluebonnet**

Tree – **Pecan**

Postcard Projects: Creative Ideas for Studying Our 50 States © 1995 Good Apple

TEXAS USA 5-95

TEXAS
The Lone Star State

Six Flags Over Texas is a large amusement park in Arlington that has rides of all types. The six flags are significant to the history of the state. Illustrate each flag and design a seventh flag to celebrate present-day Texas.

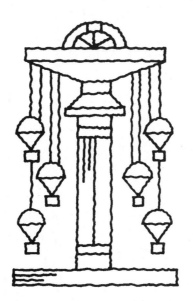

Postcard Projects: Creative Ideas for Studying Our 50 States © 1995 Good Apple

TEXAS USA 5-95

TEXAS

At Camp Verde, the United States Army once imported camels to use for transportation. The experiment failed. Find out what happened and write a humorous story about the experiment.

Postcard Projects: Creative Ideas for Studying Our 50 States © 1995 Good Apple

TEXAS

In San Antonio you can visit the Alamo. Read about this famous mission and the battle that took place there. Imagine you are a negotiator and propose a peaceful settlement.

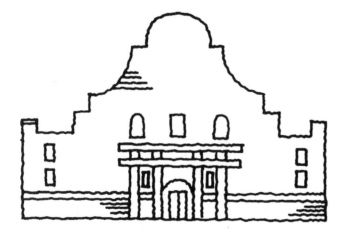

Postcard Projects: Creative Ideas for Studying Our 50 States © 1995 Good Apple

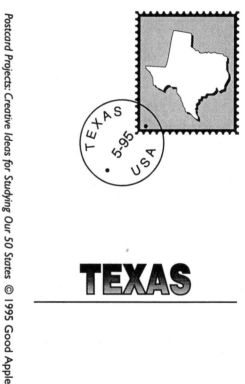

TEXAS

NASA's Mission Control Center is located in Houston. Write a conversation that could take place between an alien and a radio operator at Mission Control. Include some facts that you have researched about Mission Control in your make-believe conversation.

Postcard Projects: Creative Ideas for Studying Our 50 States © 1995 Good Apple

TEXAS
_____

Texas longhorn cattle drives and cowboys are all part of early Texas history. On a large sheet of paper, draw and label all the equipment a cowboy would have needed in the early West.

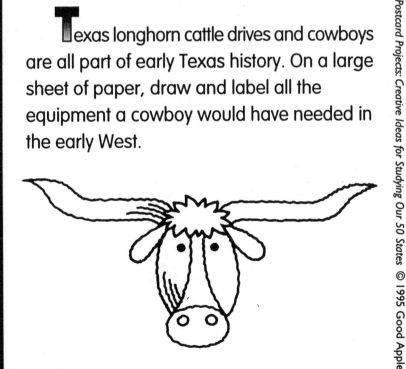

Postcard Projects: Creative Ideas for Studying Our 50 States © 1995 Good Apple

TEXAS
_____

Capital – **Salt Lake City**

Size – **82,076 square miles**
(rank: 12)

Statehood – **January 4, 1896**
(45th state)

Song – **"Utah, We Love Thee"**

Bird – **California gull**

Flower – **Sego lily**

Tree – **Blue spruce**

Postcard Projects: Creative Ideas for Studying Our 50 States © 1995 Good Apple

UTAH
The Beehive State

Petroglyphs can be found in Capitol Reef National Park. What are petroglyphs? Find several examples and record them on a large sheet of paper. Tell where they are found and what scientists believe they say.

Postcard Projects: Creative Ideas for Studying Our 50 States © 1995 Good Apple

UTAH

Great Salt Lake is the nation's largest inland sea. Write a report telling how the lake was formed and why it is so salty.

Postcard Projects: Creative Ideas for Studying Our 50 States © 1995 Good Apple

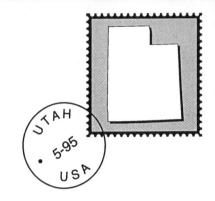

UTAH

Dinosaur National Monument is located in Utah. Make a book of dinosaur illustrations showing the types that have been excavated there. Include an informative paragraph about each one.

Postcard Projects: Creative Ideas for Studying Our 50 States © 1995 Good Apple

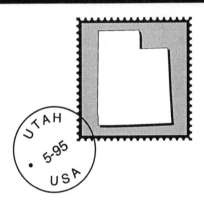

UTAH

Salt Lake City is the center of the Mormon religion. Read about the Mormons and make a captioned time line of their history.

Postcard Projects: Creative Ideas for Studying Our 50 States © 1995 Good Apple

UTAH _____

Many land speed records have been set on the Bonneville Salt Flats near Wendover. Find out why and read about the vehicles that set these records. Then design a vehicle that might set a new record.

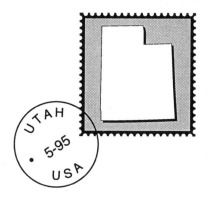

Postcard Projects: Creative Ideas for Studying Our 50 States © 1995 Good Apple

UTAH _____

Capital – **Montpelier**

Size – **9,273 square miles**
(rank: 43)

Statehood – **March 4, 1791**
(14th state)

Song – **"Hail, Vermont!"**

Bird – **Hermit thrush**

Flower – **Red clover**

Tree – **Sugar maple**

Postcard Projects: Creative Ideas for Studying Our 50 States © 1995 Good Apple

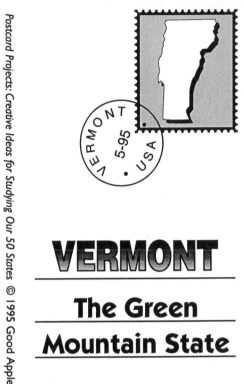

VERMONT

The Green
Mountain State

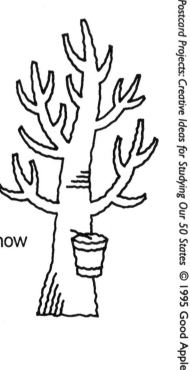

The maple syrup industry is important to Vermont. Find out how maple syrup is made. Make an illustrated flow chart to show the process.

Postcard Projects: Creative Ideas for Studying Our 50 States © 1995 Good Apple

VERMONT

Ethan Allen and the Green Mountain Boys are famous American Revolutionary War heroes. Find out about them and write a report.

Postcard Projects: Creative Ideas for Studying Our 50 States © 1995 Good Apple

VERMONT

Much of the state's income comes from granite and marble quarries. To help the state economy, list as many uses for granite and marble as you can. Be creative with your ideas.

MANY USES OF GRANITE AND MARBLE

Postcard Projects: Creative Ideas for Studying Our 50 States © 1995 Good Apple

VERMONT

Danville is the site of a dowser's convention held each year in the middle of September. Find out what dowsers do. Write a short report telling what you learned and give a "dowsing" demonstration to your class.

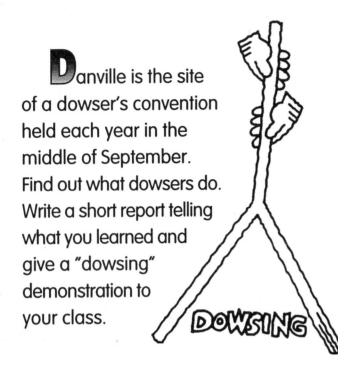

DOWSING

Postcard Projects: Creative Ideas for Studying Our 50 States © 1995 Good Apple

VERMONT

5-95

VERMONT

USA

The highways in Vermont are dotted with numerous historic-site markers. One such historic site is Lake Champlain. Make a postcard of this site and, on the reverse side, tell how the lake got its name.

NEW YORK

VERMONT

LAKE CHAMPLAIN

Postcard Projects: Creative Ideas for Studying Our 50 States © 1995 Good Apple

VERMONT

5-95

VERMONT

USA

Capital – **Richmond**

Size – **39,700 square miles
(rank: 36)**

Statehood – **June 25, 1788
(10th state)**

Song – **"Carry Me Back to
Old Virginia"**

Bird – **Cardinal**

Flower – **Dogwood flower**

Tree – **Dogwood**

Postcard Projects: Creative Ideas for Studying Our 50 States © 1995 Good Apple

VIRGINIA

Old

Dominion

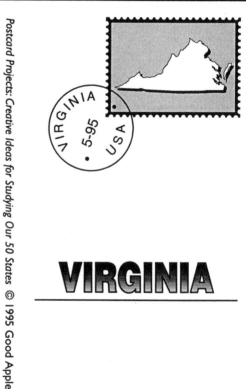

St. Paul's Church in Norfolk still has a British cannonball embedded in its wall. Write a newspaper account telling how this happened. Be sure to include a catchy headline for your article.

Postcard Projects: Creative Ideas for Studying Our 50 States © 1995 Good Apple

VIRGINIA

Jamestown, Williamsburg, and Yorktown are three of America's most historic sites. Choose one to research and record your findings in an illustrated brochure.

Postcard Projects: Creative Ideas for Studying Our 50 States © 1995 Good Apple

VIRGINIA

Mount Vernon, home of George Washington, and Monticello, home of Thomas Jefferson, are located in Virginia. Make a chart comparing and contrasting these two plantations.

Postcard Projects: Creative Ideas for Studying Our 50 States © 1995 Good Apple

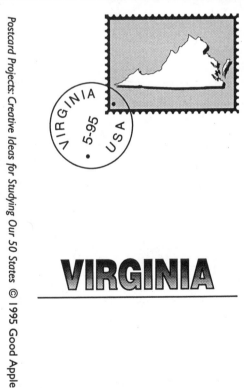

VIRGINIA

From Fort Monroe, you could have watched the battle between the Monitor and the Merrimac. Illustrate the two ships and tell why the battle was so important.

Postcard Projects: Creative Ideas for Studying Our 50 States © 1995 Good Apple

VIRGINIA

5-95

USA

VIRGINIA

Besides being the third United States President, Thomas Jefferson made many other contributions. Make a list explaining these other accomplishments.

Postcard Projects: Creative Ideas for Studying Our 50 States © 1995 Good Apple

VIRGINIA

5-95

USA

VIRGINIA

Capital – **Olympia**

Size – **66,512 square miles (rank: 20)**

Statehood – **November 11, 1889 (42nd state)**

Song – **"Washington, My Home"**

Bird – **Willow goldfinch**

Flower – **Rhododendron**

Tree – **Western hemlock**

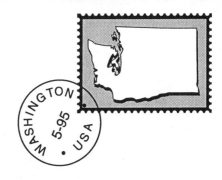

Postcard Projects: Creative Ideas for Studying Our 50 States © 1995 Good Apple

WASHINGTON

The Evergreen State

Salmon fishing is a favorite summer sport in Washington. Study the life cycle of the salmon and illustrate it on a chart.

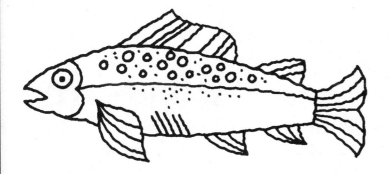

Postcard Projects: Creative Ideas for Studying Our 50 States © 1995 Good Apple

WASHINGTON

The famous cry, "Fifty-four forty or fight!" has its roots in the state of Washington. Find out its significance and find a way to explain it to the class without doing any writing.

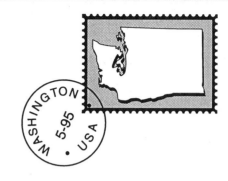

Postcard Projects: Creative Ideas for Studying Our 50 States © 1995 Good Apple

WASHINGTON

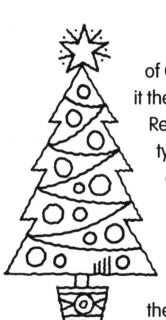

Shelton's large crop of Christmas trees makes it the "Christmas Town." Research the different types of evergreens used as Christmas trees. Make an illustrated booklet telling about each one. Include your recommendation for the best Christmas tree and give your reasons.

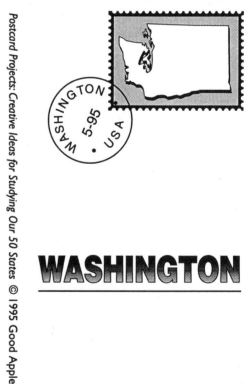

Postcard Projects: Creative Ideas for Studying Our 50 States © 1995 Good Apple

WASHINGTON

The Grand Coulee Dam serves what once was the largest hydroelectric complex in the world. Find out how it got its name. Make an illustrated poster telling what you learned.

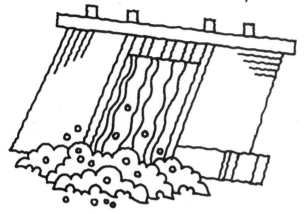

Postcard Projects: Creative Ideas for Studying Our 50 States © 1995 Good Apple

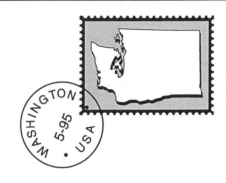

WASHINGTON WASHINGTON

In May 1980, Mount St. Helens erupted. Research the causes of volcanic eruptions. Make a cut-away model of a volcano and explain why and how volcanic eruptions occur.

Postcard Projects: Creative Ideas for Studying Our 50 States © 1995 Good Apple

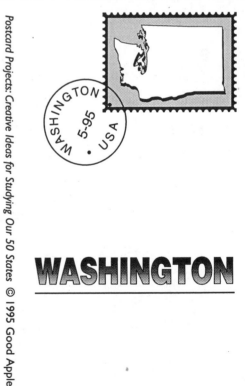

WASHINGTON

Capital – **Charleston**

Size – **24,124 square miles (rank: 41)**

Statehood – **June 20, 1863 (35th state)**

Song – **"The West Virginia Hills" and two others**

Bird – **Cardinal**

Flower – **Rhododendron**

Tree – **Sugar maple**

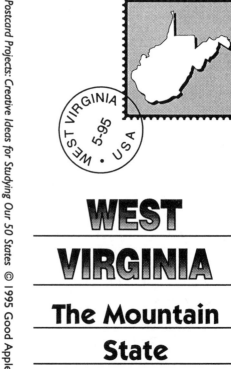

Postcard Projects: Creative Ideas for Studying Our 50 States © 1995 Good Apple

WEST VIRGINIA 5-95 · USA

WEST VIRGINIA

The Mountain State

West Virginia is the glass marble manufacturing center of the United States. Make a chart illustrating the steps in manufacturing a marble. Then teach the game of marbles to a friend and give a demonstration to the class.

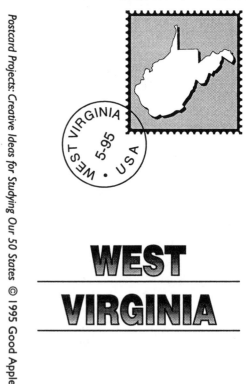

Postcard Projects: Creative Ideas for Studying Our 50 States © 1995 Good Apple

WEST VIRGINIA 5-95 · USA

WEST VIRGINIA

Harper's Ferry, where John Brown was captured, is now part of a national historic park. Find out why John Brown raided Harper's Ferry. Write an essay either agreeing or disagreeing with his ideas and methods.

Postcard Projects: Creative Ideas for Studying Our 50 States © 1995 Good Apple

WEST VIRGINIA 5-95 · USA

WEST VIRGINIA

West Virginia has this country's largest coal deposits. Make an illustrated flow chart showing how coal is formed and mined.

COAL

Postcard Projects: Creative Ideas for Studying Our 50 States © 1995 Good Apple

WEST VIRGINIA 5-95 · USA

WEST VIRGINIA

West Virginia's most popular folk hero is a giant named John Henry. Find out what made him a legend and tell the tale to your classmates. Include an illustration of John Henry at work.

Postcard Projects: Creative Ideas for Studying Our 50 States © 1995 Good Apple

WEST VIRGINIA · USA 5-95

WEST
VIRGINIA

West Virginia was once part of Virginia. Find out how and when the state split and write a newspaper article telling about it.

THE SPLIT
OF
OF VIRGINIA
AND
WEST VIRGINIA

Postcard Projects: Creative Ideas for Studying Our 50 States © 1995 Good Apple

WEST VIRGINIA · USA 5-95

WEST
VIRGINIA

Capital – **Madison**

Size – **54,424 square miles**
(rank: 25)

Statehood – **May 29, 1848**
(30th state)

Song – **"On, Wisconsin!"**

Bird – **Robin**

Flower – **Wood violet**

Tree – **Sugar maple**

Postcard Projects: Creative Ideas for Studying Our 50 States © 1995 Good Apple

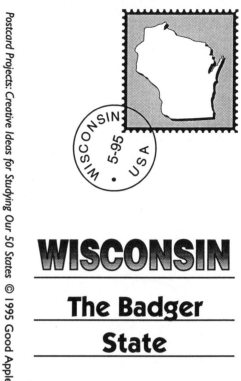

WISCONSIN

The Badger State

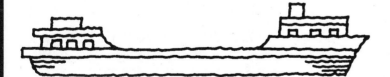 **M**any of the first settlers traveled up the Mississippi River in flat bottom boats called *bateaux*. Make a model of a bateau and tell why this was the chosen mode of transportation by early settlers.

Postcard Projects: Creative Ideas for Studying Our 50 States © 1995 Good Apple

WISCONSIN

Wisconsin is known as "The Badger State." Find out how it got this name and make an illustrated poster explaining the origin of the name.

Postcard Projects: Creative Ideas for Studying Our 50 States © 1995 Good Apple

WISCONSIN

Wisconsin is famous for its cheese production. Make a flow chart illustrating how cheese is made. Also, tell how different types of cheese are made.

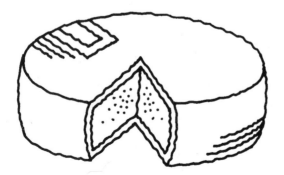

Postcard Projects: Creative Ideas for Studying Our 50 States © 1995 Good Apple

WISCONSIN

The Peshtigo forest fire killed 1,200 people in 1871. Read about this devastating fire and compare it to the Chicago fire in 1871. Report your findings in a chart or a Venn diagram.

Postcard Projects: Creative Ideas for Studying Our 50 States © 1995 Good Apple

WISCONSIN

The Circus World Museum is in Baraboo, site of the Ringling Brothers Circus winter home. Research circus history. Report your findings in an illustrated booklet.

Postcard Projects: Creative Ideas for Studying Our 50 States © 1995 Good Apple

WISCONSIN

Capital – **Cheyenne**

Size – **96,988 square miles**
(rank: 9)

Statehood – **July 10, 1890**
(44th state)

Song – **"Wyoming"**

Bird – **Meadowlark**

Flower – **Indian paintbrush**

Tree – **Cottonwood**

Postcard Projects: Creative Ideas for Studying Our 50 States © 1995 Good Apple

WYOMING

MYOMING 5-95 USA

WYOMING

The Equality
State

General William Ashley established an annual "rendezvous" for fur trappers in 1825. Pretend you are attending a "rendezvous" and write a diary telling all that you saw and did.

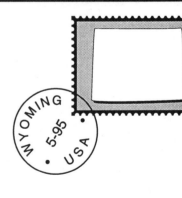

DIARY

RENDEZVOUS FOR FUR TRAPPERS

Postcard Projects: Creative Ideas for Studying Our 50 States © 1995 Good Apple

MYOMING 5-95 USA

WYOMING

Tourism is one of the major industries in Wyoming. Design a travel brochure illustrating the many attractions in the state.

Postcard Projects: Creative Ideas for Studying Our 50 States © 1995 Good Apple

WYOMING

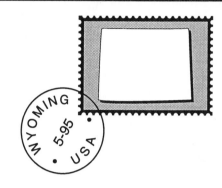

The people who created the National Elk Refuge near Jackson were considered to be ahead of their time. Find out why and explain why animal refuges of this type are becoming increasingly important.

Postcard Projects: Creative Ideas for Studying Our 50 States © 1995 Good Apple

WYOMING

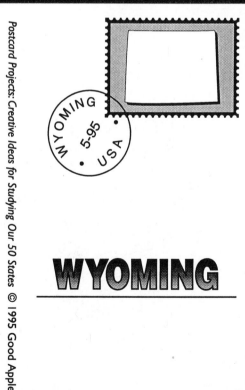

Yellowstone National Park, the nation's first national park, is located in the northwest corner of the state. Plan a one-week vacation for you and your family to Yellowstone. Make a poster illustrating and telling about all the things you will see and do.

Postcard Projects: Creative Ideas for Studying Our 50 States © 1995 Good Apple

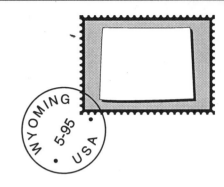

WYOMING

It took four treaties for the United States to get the land that makes up Wyoming. Find out what these four treaties were and in a report tell a little about each one.

Postcard Projects: Creative Ideas for Studying Our 50 States © 1995 Good Apple

WYOMING

SIZE RANK ORDER

1 - Alaska		26 - Florida	
2 - Texas		27 - Arkansas	
3 - California		28 - Alabama	
4 - Montana		29 - North Carolina	
5 - New Mexico		30 - New York	
6 - Arizona		31 - Mississippi	
7 - Nevada		32 - Pennsylvania	
8 - Colorado		33 - Louisiana	
9 - Wyoming		34 - Tennessee	
10 - Oregon		35 - Ohio	
11 - Idaho		36 - Virginia	
12 - Utah		37 - Kentucky	
13 - Kansas		38 - Indiana	
14 - Minnesota		39 - Maine	
15 - Nebraska		40 - South Carolina	
16 - South Dakota		41 - West Virginia	
17 - North Dakota		42 - Maryland	
18 - Missouri		43 - Vermont	
19 - Oklahoma		44 - New Hampshire	
20 - Washington		45 - Massachusetts	
21 - Georgia		46 - New Jersey	
22 - Michigan		47 - Hawaii	
23 - Iowa		48 - Connecticut	
24 - Illinois		49 - Delaware	
25 - Wisconsin		50 - Rhode Island	

STATEHOOD ORDER

1 - Delaware	26 - Michigan
2 - Pennsylvania	27 - Florida
3 - New Jersey	28 - Texas
4 - Georgia	29 - Iowa
5 - Connecticut	30 - Wisconsin
6 - Massachusetts	31 - California
7 - Maryland	32 - Minnesota
8 - South Carolina	33 - Oregon
9 - New Hampshire	34 - Kansas
10 - Virginia	35 - West Virginia
11 - New York	36 - Nevada
12 - North Carolina	37 - Nebraska
13 - Rhode Island	38 - Colorado
14 - Vermont	39 - North Dakota
15 - Kentucky	40 - South Dakota
16 - Tennessee	41 - Montana
17 - Ohio	42 - Washington
18 - Louisiana	43 - Idaho
19 - Indiana	44 - Wyoming
20 - Mississippi	45 - Utah
21 - Illinois	46 - Oklahoma
22 - Alabama	47 - New Mexico
23 - Maine	48 - Arizona
24 - Missouri	49 - Alaska
25 - Arkansas	50 - Hawaii